Breaking Up
with
TOXICITY

A simplified workbook to recognize toxicity and
reclaim your power from
toxic people

Maria Shkreli, LMHC

This book contains summarized information relating to mental health. It is not intended to replace medical advice and should not be used to supplement mental health care. All efforts have been made to ensure the accuracy of the information provided. Both publisher and author disclaim any liability for any methods applied or suggested in this guide. Characters and incidents portrayed in this book have been changed to protect the privacy of individuals. In order to maintain their anonymity, I have not used nor implied the names of individuals and places they reside. I may have changed some identifying characteristics and details to further protect their identity. Any resemblance to actual persons, living or dead, or actual events, is purely coincidental.

First Series: September 2022

Printed in the United States of America.

ISBN- 979-8-218-06974-2

Contents

You will learn about:
- Trauma
- Toxic relationships & traits
- Trauma bonding
- Anxious Attachments
- Dependent Personality Disorder
- Narcissistic Personality Disorder, Narcissistic personality traits
- Borderline Personality Disorder
- Boundaries and communication
- Irrational thoughts and beliefs

Use this book as a supplement, if you are in therapy. If needed, **professional assistance is your best approach.**

Maria Shkreli is a licensed Mental Health Therapist and author practicing in Pleasantville, New York. (therapy4growth.com) Her specialties include working with Anxiety, ADHD, Family Conflict, Couple Conflict, Toxic Relationships, and Personality Diagnoses.   Additionally, she is the author of Negative Thoughts Don't = A POSITIVE LIFE, My 14-Day Anxiety Challenge, Colorful Emotion, Help! My Anxious Middle Schooler, The DSM-5 MisUNDERSTOOD, The Simplified NCMHCE Study Guide, and the College Student's Guide to Understanding the DSM—5.

To all the people in my life who knocked me down and helped me break the cycle of toxicity

Forward

Why this workbook happened.

I am sure many of you have already purchased many books and talked to others about toxic relationships, and this self-help book is another one to add to your collection. *Why do I make these mistakes? Why can't I break the cycle?* One reason is because people who are over-empathic are easy targets for toxic people. I spent years searching for the same answers and learned when an individual is ready to challenge themselves, they will do the work needed.

There are countless books about toxic relationships – some are complex, some are simple. My goal is to add a simple yet robust option for people to learn the strategies I use in my support groups and individual counseling sessions with my clients. The information, recommendations, and techniques in this book will assist in educating you on what toxicity is and will help you learn how to identify unhealthy relationship patterns. It will help you to identify your own unhealthy patterns, and to implement methods to reduce and manage the impact these relationships have in your life.

This book isn't written in clinical terms; I don't want to overwhelm you. The strategies and methods you'll discover in the next few pages are a way to start actively helping you address your understanding of toxic relationships. Eventually they will help you work toward a happier and healthier way of coping without getting caught in the cycle of chaos with toxic people. I've taken certain sections from other books I've written and added them to this workbook because they bring valuable information and clarity that have helped end cycles and chapters for both my own and my clients' journey of healing.

I will be as informative as I can to help you learn why you are drawn to these people, how to recognize the impact they have on you, and how to reduce and eventually eliminate this impact.

I am excited for you as you embark on a journey of healing, reflection, inspiration, self-exploration, and finding your strength. With this workbook, you bring your own reflections into each page to promote healing from toxicity in your life and to find your peace and authentic self through your own work and time.

It's not always intimate relationships - it can be friends, co-workers, family, and bosses. It doesn't matter what time they were in your life, what matters is that you broke free. Because of these people you developed the strength to take back your life. You were shattered without knowing you were shattered. We all know people with traits of personality diagnosis, and they are part of our lives; with firm boundaries and good communication, they can remain in our lives. However, Narcissists will have a detrimental effect on us. Sadly, we spend so much time thinking and hoping they will change, but the reality is that they will never change. *We* have to change – redirect focus on ourselves in order to save ourselves. Cutting off these people is when your healing begins. That healing is a long journey, so be kind to yourself, because it took years to recognize what happened to you. It's not your fault.

Broken

We become quiet as he comes into the room. We can always tell when he's nearby; we sense him. We walk on eggshells every day. Why? Because we fear what he may do; we've seen what he's done to others. He spreads rumors and lies. He has two faces. One day it is a face of fake sweetness, and another day it's a face of pure hatred. He's a wrath of disturbing emotions. He guides to you follow his path and when he has you in his web, he controls you; controls you with his words, and his threats. He controls you in a way that's unhealthy and damaging. We know this and we will live in fear, paranoia and pain. Our pain is deep and confusing, and we are uncertain if we are crazy. Maybe it is us; maybe we did say that, maybe we did do that? It's always our fault; all the justifying means nothing – our weakness is that we are always trying to prove ourselves.

He bullies us all the time, and we know it. He speaks strongly with an intimidating tone, but at other times he's a rambling idiot; his madness is chaos. He yells at us and makes us feel small and tells us we are useless people; *"You are nobodies without me, that's why you're here with me. You have no courage to leave because you will never find it better than here."* No one can touch him or stand up to him, and he knows this. Why are we afraid? We lie because we are afraid and to protect each other. Why do we choose to let him belittle and degrade us, and fear him? He controls so many lives through lies, deceit, and manipulation, and we know this. But why don't we run? We need to run as fast as we can from this monster. He's created this superpowered person – the almighty who knows it all – and sadly, we bow to him. He expects this from us. He reminds us he can't do wrong – he is better than us and will always be better than us. He will destroy us. He's a superpower of pure hurt, hate, envy, jealousy, and evil.

At the end we don't hate; we choose to no longer fear because we are people with a good soul, and we choose to love ourselves.

My journey and my client's journey is of courage and determination. I believe when one is ready, they will be able to say the same. Until then, they will continue to work through their pain, and one day (and that day will come!) they will be freed and live a happy life. "Healed" consists of many different people, different times, different relationships in our lives all put together. It's not something to be sad over, it's something to embrace – because having the ability to overcome brings us to a place that words can't describe. It's a forgiving and loving place.

I look forward to hearing from you when that time comes.

Healed

Why? I was afraid. You hurt me. You scared me. You spread rumors. You kept others away from me. I hid. I cried. I lost myself. I saw the dark side of loneliness. I saw the dark side of death. I wanted to run. Run so far from everyone. I wanted to hide. I couldn't hide. I wanted you to feel the pain I felt. I wanted to die. Why? Why did you hurt me? Your words. Your lies. You left me all alone. My soul was gone. I had no fight to live. I was all alone. I was in hell. I lived hell every day. Did you ever wonder about me? I lost my strength. My fears overtook my life. I watched over in fear. I slept in fear. I heard voices inside my head telling me I was nobody. At times I believed I was nobody. You told me over and over I meant nothing to anyone. I believed this. You told me I was better off dead. Why? Why did you hurt me? What lesson is this? What cruelty is this?

One day, I decided not to let you win. I found myself within myself. I found my courage. I found my confidence. I found my strength. I no longer believed no one loved me. I valued my life. I valued myself. I wasn't going to defeat you with hurtful words. I defeated you by deciding not to let you hurt me with your words or your actions.

I had to look deep inside and find this on my own. I did. It was a harrowing journey. It was a lonely journey. I was scared. I doubted I could do this. I found my way. I worked hard and found the love I needed. That love was to love me first. I found my voice. I found me. I walked without fear. I slept without fear. I found the courage to live again. My heart gave me the ability to fight and overcome my struggles caused by you. I learned I allowed it. I don't fear you. I feel sorrow for you. Through your pain, I found my strength.

Thank you for my struggles.
My struggle made me who I am today.
I am my life.
I am my gift.
I am me.
I am a fighter.

Self Awareness

Before you start this workbook, I'd like you to take time and answer the questions on the next pages. Please don't read ahead in the book before you answer them.

Once you complete the workbook, you can return to these questions and read what you wrote before you started – How would you answer differently now? What did you learn?

Describe what love looks like for you:

What does a toxic relationship look like to you?

How do you work through relationship challenges?

Can you be yourself in your friendship(s) and relationship(s)? Why or why not?

Do you obsess over disappointment, hurt, or people? What goes on when this happens?

When you argue with your partner, family or friends, how do you see the issue? Do you view it as 'you against them' or 'you and them against the problem?'

People spend a lot of time worrying about what other people think of them, and about their own worthiness - are we enough? When people think like this, they spend part of their life comparing themselves to others, people-pleasing, and proving. The only person that can let go of this is you. Address shame:

Talk about it.
Who are you when you feel shame?

How do you protect yourself?

What negative experiences seem to repeat in your life?

What are you currently worried about?

What life-changing, devasting event(s) occurred in your life?

Who is the person you hurt the most?

How would you describe empathy?

How would you describe manipulation and gaslighting?

Describe what you know about Narcissistic Personality Disorder:

Describe what you know about Borderline Personality Disorder:

Describe what you know about Trauma Bonding:

Describe what you know about Anxious Attachment:

Describe what you know about Avoidant Attachment:

Describe what you know about Fearful Avoidant Attachment:

Describe what you know about Generalized Anxiety:

Describe Dependent Personality Disorder:

Describe what you know about irrational thought patterns:

Describe what you know about negative core beliefs:

How good do you consider your mental health to be?

Showing up for you

Every experience in life gives you the opportunity to learn and rise from its challenges – to choose different paths or choose to stay stuck in unhealthy pasts. You decide each day how you are going to show up for yourself.

Without sounding too spiritual, we each have an assignment here and we can choose how we handle these assignments. The most important assignment we have is showing up. Once you decide to show up, your old stories and experience become the past, because you've made the choice to be in your power and change your life.

So, how do you do this?

Step 1. Take a clear look at your life; identify your trauma and fears.
Step 2. Recognize that if you don't work on yourself, you will stay stuck and you will continue your patterns.
Step 3. Be kind to yourself; don't find fault and blame. You are learning to be the best you can be.
Step 4. Learn to own your role in life. You can't control what other people do. You are the only one that can make it better.
Step 5. Don't focus on fixing the other person.
Step 6. Remember that finding fault in others is work for yourself. No matter how someone treats and talks to you – you allow this.
Step 7. Show up for *you* each day.

Let's begin to learn about toxicity.

What is Toxicity?

Toxicity is a relationship that is unhealthy and dysfunctional. Additionally, it is a relationship that makes a person feel demeaned, unsupported, and/or attacked. The toxicity can exist in one person or both people when reacting in very damaging ways, without consideration or respect for the other person's feelings. These behaviors can be harmful to one or both people.

What is a toxic relationship?

A toxic relationship is a relationship that is emotionally or mentally damaging. This type of relationship is defined by qualities of domination, submission, fear and deception.

A toxic relationship may not have started this way. Oftentimes it starts out happy and supportive. Over time, as the toxicity slowly occurs, it leaves a person feeling emotionally drained and stressed.

We have all seen toxic people drawn to reasonable people, and all of us have likely had (or have) at least one person in our lives who has damaged us and left us to question – *what did I do?* Additionally, some of these people are parents, children, family, friends, or coworkers. Damage from toxic people can be subtle – from little lies, to your constantly adjusting your own behaviors to avoid conflict. When this happens most of the time, that means it's them and not you.

Every relationship has good and bad days, but when bad days start outnumbering the good ones, it's time take a closer look at what's going on or it's time to move on. When a relationship is making you question your priorities or forcing you to make changes that cause you to compromise your individuality, it is a good time to quit. Being stressed due to your relationship can affect not only your mental health, but your physical health as well. The inability to sleep, anxiety, and feeling irritable around your partner are additional signs that you should consider questioning why you are stuck yet still staying.

In these relationships, conflict easily arises and at least one person tries to minimize the other person's feelings and perspective. There is a lack of support, verbal and psychological abuse, and manipulative behavior that leaves the other person mentally drained.

Being able to spot these harmful behaviors is the first step in learning to start to minimize the impact they have on your life. Learning about toxic people may not change what they do, but you will change how you work through it and not allow it to affect your quality of life.

Where do toxic behaviors come from?

There is no easy answer to this question, as there are many different causes. It is said that these behaviors are learned in childhood and can be experienced in adulthood. What we do know is that anyone can exhibit toxic behaviors. Toxic behaviors are part of personalities, learned in our environment and relationships. Without realizing it, we tend to "normalize" these unhealthy behaviors, and a person's perception becomes warped and lacks understanding of a healthy relationship.

Toxic people tend to bring down others to boost their own self-worth, although they are usually unaware of this unconscious need to hurt those in their lives. Why? Because they don't feel good about themselves. We all have a toxic person in our life. Sometimes we can manage these relationships with a healthy approach and sometimes we succumb to the toxicity and find ourselves stuck in it.

Do I attract toxic people?

Can you relate to the following?

Recently you made a new friend at a party. You thought things went well and that this could be a good friendship. Well, you were wrong, and this person is actually a very toxic person. They were criticizing everything about your life; you found yourself not expressing how you felt because of what you thought they were going to say.

You have been dating someone for ten months. You hit it off from the start and thought they were nice, caring and a great listener and supporter when you needed one. You were totally wrong; this person was toxic. They were a control freak – didn't listen to your opinions, threw tantrums when they were angry, and got passive-aggressive when you argued.

You wonder, *"How did this happen?"* You think to yourself, *"Why do I attract toxic people? What is wrong with me? Do I give off certain vibes or qualities that toxic people look for in their victims?"*

Toxic people are part of our lives. Understanding why someone is toxic and why you are attracted to each other means learning about certain traits you possess and events that may have affected your life. Now, thinking about the question "Do I attract toxic people," I am sure you know your answer. Simply said, if you answer "Yes," then the answer is, Yes, something is wrong. You attract toxic people because of certain traits they find attractive about you. Because of these traits, you need to realize your behaviors and actions and learn how to challenge them so that you can take and keep your power. So, you ask, what are these traits? I mention a few in the section about narcissists. One reason toxic people are attracted to you is because of your positive attitude and healthy ability to see others' perspectives and have a healthy balance in life. Toxic people are not only intrigued by your type of person, but they are also threatened by your ability. They want to victimize and control you to take away those traits, which gives them the ability to take away your power. Yes, pretty powerful, I agree. So how do you take your power back? Educate yourself about toxic people, and work on learning about yourself and any toxic traits you may have. And always make working on *you* your focus.

Now if you are ready to begin your journey, let's move on and learn about toxic people and *you*.

Red flags

While toxic relationships take on many different red flags, common signs include emotional manipulation, disrespect, verbal abuse, and feeling lonely when you're together. Only you can determine if the relationship is toxic and threating to your emotional, psychological or physical well-being.

The following are a few indications of red flags to watch for in a relationship (this can also include relationships with friends, family and coworkers):

Walking on eggshells – you find yourself walking on eggshells all the time for fear of upsetting your partner.

It's always about them – your relationship is always about them; praising, supporting, listening, and rarely and/or ever about you.

You ditch your values – in order to keep the relationship, you ditch your interests and friendships and compromise your own values.

Being made fun of – your partner makes fun of your sensitivity, insults you, makes fun of flaws.

Constant drama – you always feel a sense of distress around them as chaos and drama seem to follow them.

Lack of boundaries – you struggle to remain emotionally, mentally, or physically clear, as your partner oversteps all boundaries.

Self-absorption – your partner is always in their own problems, goals, and desires, with no mutual ground between you.

Jealous of your accomplishments – your partner feels they need to drag you down because of your success.

Always taking their side – you always feel you need to agree with them to avoid negative repercussions.

Your self-worth – you feel unworthy and worthless while being around your partner.

Scorekeeping – your partner keeps scores for all your wrongdoings, and instead of moving past this, there are constant fights and arguments.

Justifying bad behavior – you constantly excuse or justify your partner's display of selfish or nasty behavior.

Emotional inequality – you always feel like you must do all the emotional work in the relationship while your partner presents as immature, rude, unreliable, or cold.

Lack of responsibility – your partner is entitled and feels they don't need to be responsible for their mistakes or their part in the relationship.

Can't speak your mind – unable to speak your feelings, needs or thoughts without worrying about the consequences.

Defined roles – roles are expected to be followed, and if they aren't, there is a fear of implications on the relationship.

Always agreeing – you always agree with your partner to avoid conflict.

Contempt – made to feel worthless, unworthy, vile, not respected, by use of negative and condescending tones, including sarcasm and eye rolling.

Being made fun of – you are made fun of by name-calling or insults

Deception – your partner lacks truthfulness and you recognize that the lies are always turned around to make you sound crazy.

It's always your fault – your partner always blames you for anything and everything that goes wrong. Situations are turned around so that things that go wrong are your fault.

Domination – control issues exist in the relationship, resulting in emotional psychological 'games.'

Gaslighting – this is a form of manipulation that makes you question your own sanity. Gaslighting consists of the other person insisting that something you recall never happened, telling you that you are delusional because they never said something you confronted them with, accusing you of being the one with control issues and/or anger issues.

Manipulation – this is a form of persuasion where the person uses different tactics to get what they want.

Can a toxic relationship work?

Many people think toxic relationships are doomed, but that may not always be the case. If both people want to change and recognize their roles in the relationship, it can change. If one person isn't invested in creating a healthy relationship, odds are, it won't happen, and this is when the other person has to consider their next step.

If healing is possible, it depends on one's circumstance and how much damage was done to one or both people or to a family. The healing of a toxic relationship can only happen through a conscious decision of effort to work on yourself, and if your friend, partner or family does the same.

Signs that someone can work through a toxic relationship with their partner, family, or friend:

Accepting responsibility
When both people know the relationship has issues and they want to work on this together. Both people will recognize the past, including behaviors that harmed the relationship. Both people have to accept their role in contributing to the toxicity.

You both want to invest
If both people want to invest in the work and time, that is an indication that the relationship can change for the better. You will need to take the time to talk through the issues in the relationship.

Eliminating the blaming
Both people self-reflect on their roles and commit to working on understanding why the reaction behavior occurred. Both people learn to accept their own roles without looking to blame the other person.

Resist controlling the other person
Avoid trying to control the other person and influencing them to think or behave in a way you desire.

Mind games and manipulation have to stop
Many people are guilty of this. When working on rebuilding a relationship, all mind games, gaslighting, and manipulation must stop.

Seeking professional help
It's okay to seek help. Not all people know how to work through a relationship. Seeking outside help can be beneficial.

List the toxic relationships in your life: partner, family, friends, colleagues. Describe how these relationships affect(ed) your quality of life.

Let's move on and learn about toxic personalities.

What is Narcissistic Personality Disorder?

You've heard the word 'narcissistic' thrown around so often that it's become a popular terminology in psychology and in social media. Many perceive narcissism to describe people who have inflated egos and are only interested in themselves. This has some truth to it, but there's more to it than that. Some narcissists do not always have inflated egos, but a true narcissist does have a need for admiration, patterns of grandiosity, a lack of empathy, arrogance, and envy. And to throw a curve at you, there is a difference between Narcissistic Personality Disorder and narcissistic personality traits. Someone with narcissistic personality traits falls on a spectrum and has less frequency, intensity and duration. Someone with narcissistic personality traits can address their behavior when they recognize it's unhealthy, but someone who is diagnosed with Narcissistic Personality Disorder cannot recognize this – this is a mental illness. So, what does this mean? Not all narcissists have a personality disorder diagnosis.

I highly recommend that you educate yourself on this diagnosis as part of your healing, so you can work on your own mental health. The focus isn't on educating you about the diagnosis so you can change the narcissist, it's about educating yourself so you can remove the personalization (not take things personally) and realize and accept that changing the other person isn't possible.

Narcissistic Personality Disorder is a formal mental health diagnosis which is usually diagnosed when someone presents five of nine symptoms of the diagnosis. If a person does not present five symptoms and it doesn't affect their quality of life or relationships, that is when narcissism traits are part of someone's personality. Having these traits can occur on a spectrum and can actually be healthy for people, as they can provide confidence in exploring life, taking risks and having relationships

Now let's learn about the difference between Narcissistic Personality Disorder and narcissistic personality traits. This is important to know because many people label others without knowing the difference, and don't realize this difference changes the level of toxicity of a relationship. Someone with narcissism can recognize these qualities in themselves, and with therapy can reduce the impact it has in their lives and the lives of those around them. Why is this important in a relationship? Because you can have a better chance of working out the issues that exist between you.

Narcissistic Personality Disorder
vs.
Narcissism as a personality trait

Narcissistic Personality Disorder – a diagnosed mental health disorder

No empathy
Grandiose/sense of entitlement
Hot/cold moods, behaviors
Love bomb – they "explode" with affection after only knowing you a short time
Inflated sense of self
Need for admiration
Believe they are superior to others
Have little regard for other people's feelings
Alienate friends and family
Depressed
A deep sense of shame and humiliation
Target people with codependent tendencies

Narcissists are charming, confident, bullies, afraid of loneliness They have no empathy, no quality of friendship. Interestingly, narcissists have low self-esteem and can be very vulnerable to their egos. They can be easily humiliated and become very angry. Additionally, they are very hesitant to engage in tasks that can humiliate them.

Narcissism – personality traits, not a mental illness

Obnoxious
Sense of entitlement
Self-centered
Big ego
Don't always feel shame or remorse
Manipulate people to get what they want
Little or no empathy
These people don't have an awareness of what they do and have some empathy and kindness. They do not exploit other people maliciously and are not self-absorbed in all areas of life.

The major distinction between the narcissist and Narcissistic Personality Disorder is that the narcissist is not mentally ill.

Narcissists and therapy
Narcissists rarely seek therapy, because they do not want to change. If a narcissist seeks therapy, it's usually forced on them because of a relationship, their children, employment, and/or court mandated. Even then, if they attend therapy a narcissist won't stay there.

Without getting too clinical, Narcissistic Personality Disorder presents with the following criteria:

Grandiose – They feel more important than they are, and their sense of importance is usually out of proportion to what they have actually achieved. They tend to show off and brag about achievements.

Exploit others – They take advantage of people around them to gain something for themselves.

Sense of entitlement – They need special treatment. They expect people to know how special they are and feel people need to show them the respect they deserve.

Lack of empathy – They are unable to understand the emotional needs of other people. They genuinely don't understand others' viewpoints.

Preoccupation with fantasies – They fantasize about their intelligence, greatness, power, or looks. They will compare themselves with someone who is successful.

They are superior – They feel they are special and the most important person in the room. They feel they can only associate with people just as important as them.

Excessive admiration – They need to show off so they can be praised and admired by others. This need feeds their feelings that they are special.

Envious of others – They believe people are envious of them because they are so special and are envious of people who have more than they do.

Arrogant – They can be very condescending; they talk down to people.

There is only one official diagnosis for NPD, but five different types have been identified:

Overt narcissism – also known as 'grandiose presentation.' People confuse this with Narcissistic Personality Disorder when the person tends to be outgoing, entitled, arrogant, overbearing, outgoing, competitive, and have an exaggerated sense of self.

Covert narcissism – also known as 'vulnerable narcissism.' This person doesn't fit the pattern of a narcissist, but some of the common traits include being introverted, experiencing high anxiety, shame and depression; being insecure, defensive, avoidant, highly sensitive; having a need for constant reassurance; tending to play a victim role and having low self-esteem.

Antagonistic narcissism – a subtype of overt narcissism. They are arrogant, take advantage of others, continuously compete with others and are prone to arguing. They focus on rivalry and competition. They are less likely to forgive and have lower levels of trust in others.

Communal narcissism – insincerely caring in an effort to garner attention with a communal environment, such as participating in events, sports, charities and showing concern for societal needs.

Malignant narcissism – aggressive, paranoid, egocentric aggression, and potentially most abusive. **(most extreme NPD)**

Effects of narcissism on relationships

The effects of emotional abuse and narcissistic abuse can vary depending on the length of the relationship and can be mild to severe. Some people can heal from this abuse while others can be affected for years. Once you've left a relationship, or you were discarded by someone with Narcissistic Personality Disorder, it takes approximately two years to heal from the abuse after you've left the relationship.

The following are effects of this abuse:

Post-traumatic stress – A person may be triggered because of past events, hypervigilant, and need to be on guard.

Emotional symptoms – A person may experience irritability, feeling emotionless, personalization (taking everything personally), and mood swings.

Repeated cycles – A person may be easily persuaded to stay in touch with the toxic person.

Anxiety – One may experience fear and anxiety about future relationships and experience panic attacks and anxiety attacks. A person can also experience separation anxiety.

Depression – A person may develop depression, may isolate themselves, and struggle with feelings of worthlessness.

Sense of self-worth – A person's self-worth is damaged. They may have difficulty making decisions, have trust issues, and doubt themselves.

Forgiving yourself – A person may feel they deserved the treatment in the relationship and that there is something wrong with them. Self-esteem is also a battle, as people may feel they should have been a better person.

Future self – A person's goals and dreams may feel unattainable because the difficulty of focusing on a healthy mindset is challenging.

Physical symptoms – A person may experience stomachaches, headaches, nightmares, difficulty sleeping, body aches, and stress.

Cognitive symptoms – A person may have memory loss and difficulty concentrating.

Narcissist's common behaviors:

- Narcissists have secret lives.
- Narcissists lie.
- They blame you for everything.
- They ruin most holidays, trips and events.
- They trample on your boundaries.
- You can't save a narcissist. You can't make them want to be a better person, because they see nothing wrong with the way they treat people. You lose yourself trying to make them change.
- Narcissists treat each relationship differently – they will treat you differently depending on what they need from you. The present person they are with will get the most attention; this is the primary supply. The people they were with in past relationships are the secondary supply and the narcissist will reach out to these people if the primary person isn't giving them everything they need. Remember, supplies are objects to them. The primary supply will always be in their life.
- They will be in a new relationship before they end the relationship with you. They leave before you decide to leave them when they realize you are in control of you. They need to be the winner and leave you first.
- They don't want to hear how their behavior impacted you. They will criticize you on how you delivered the message. They do this because if they listen to you, they will have to take accountability and change their behavior.
- Gaslighting is to make you second guess yourself, doubt your reality and your perception.
- Narcissists' biggest fear is being exposed to others. They fear their false self being exposed and people seeing them for who they really are.
- Narcissists will punish you by withdrawing their affection and blackmail you with "You're never here for me when I need you."
- "You never gave me appreciation."
- They keep mental scoresheets of what they've done for you vs. what you have done for them.
- Having no contact with a narcissist is like cutting off the blood supply to their heart. They may pursue you because they need to regain control over you.
- They will text with "I know I'm probably the last person you want to hear from…" This is abusive, trapping you into the manipulation.

How a Narcissist ends relationships

How do narcissists end relationships? First, they are already in another relationship before they start the process of breaking up with you. Yes, there is always a secondary supply of people in their life - they don't get rid of the people in their life in case they need them back. Their common approach is to flip the ending of the relationship to make it seem like it's your fault, so they take no responsibility for ending the relationship because of how you treated them.

A Narcissist ends a relationship when:

You've become difficult to control
You don't fuel their ego
You don't fit their narrative of what they need
They are ready to move up to better dysfunction

A Narcissist can cause any of the below to occur:

Reactive abuse – When an abused person lashes out to the abuser in response to a situation that is occurring to shift the blame onto them. This is a form of manipulation by the abuser that will accuse you of being the abuser because of your overreaction. Over a period of time, this causes the abused person to wonder if in fact it is their fault. Remember, abusers are master manipulators.

Narcissistic flip – A form of gaslighting. This is when a narcissist flips the script onto you during a toxic situation. This occurs when you make a valid point during a situation and the narcissist's defense is to flip this around so that you're the one apologizing and feeling sorry for being wrong.

Reverse discard – When a narcissist wants to end a relationship with you, they need to make you look like the one at fault. With this tactic, the narcissist treats you so badly that you end up being the one breaking up with them. The reason they do this is because it makes them appear as the victim and have a good reason for moving on so quickly. This tactic allows the narcissist to be seen by others as the one who was abused.

Recognizing patterns

In this section you are going to think about the relationships in your life and identify the people in your life with whom you may have a Narcissistic relationship. Read each red flag and think about one or more situations and how you feel (felt) when you are in the presence of this person and check off the appropriate box.

You can also write the names of these people and your relationship with them – partner, family, friend, co-worker – and reflect on a past or present situation, describing how you felt. Doing this exercise this will help you recognize behaviors and patterns. I've left space in the boxes for you to write about feelings, describe experiences, and note any patterns you begin to find.

Red flags in a Narcissistic relationship	Your partner	Family	Friend
Walking on eggshells			
It's always about them			
You ditch your values			
Being made fun of			
Constant drama			
Lack of boundaries			
Self-absorption			
Jealous of your accomplishments			
Always taking their side			
Your self-worth			
Scorekeeping			
Justifying bad behavior			

Red flags in a Narcissistic relationship	Your partner	Family	Friend
Emotional inequality			
Lack of responsibility			
Can't speak your mind			
Defined roles			
Always agreeing			
Contempt			
Being made fun of			
Deception			
Domination			
Gaslighting			
Manipulation			

Self-care with a Narcissist

How can you work with someone who has narcissistic tendencies? As you know, they will try to maintain an upper hand and are very resistant to any change. Remember, you can't fix a person who has Narcissistic Personality Disorder. The focus is on you to learn not to get caught in their manipulation and chaos. One of the most effective ways to regain your power and mental health is to set very clear and defined boundaries. I cannot stress this enough, because if you don't, you will stay stuck in this situation and will be prone to staying stuck in future unhealthy situations.

1. Educate, educate, educate – This is so important because you will spend time trying to fix a narcissist, hoping they change, finding fault in yourself for not being able to change them, and ignoring the fact – they can not be changed! This is essential for your healing and growth, because your goal is to get to accepting them for who they are and stop seeing them as someone who is not narcissistic. Don't mix up a person who is narcissistic with a person who isn't.

2. Work on yourself – Build your self esteem. This will help you cope with the behaviors of a narcissist. Your mental health is important, as the manipulation will trip you up and set you back from building your self-esteem.

3. Have a voice – Do not always walk away and let them belittle and intimidate you. If you ignore them all the time, this will make it more difficult for you to have a voice. You can decide when having a voice is of value to you to use it to speak up or decide when it's not important to you. Speak your words clearly.

4. BOUNDARIES – Set boundaries about any behaviors that are hurtful and unacceptable to you and communicate them very clearly to the person. Since boundaries are usually not respected, it will be challenging to get them to respect yours. Using boundaries as an ultimatum does not work with them because they don't care, so it's your responsibility to ensure they take you seriously for your own mental health.

5. Therapy/support system – a narcissist can drain you. Find a support system or therapist. Therapy will teach you tools, provide skills, and educate you in ways to help you navigate this relationship.

The next type of toxic personality to be discussed will be Borderline Personality Disorder.

Borderline Personality Disorder

What is Borderline Personality Disorder?

This is a type of personality disorder in which the person's symptoms can cause them to present impulsive behaviors that develop into challenging relationships with partners, family members, friends, and coworkers.

What causes Borderline Personality Disorder?

Researchers aren't exactly sure of the cause, but research states that it comes from genetic predispositions combined with environmental factors. A person's risk of environmental factors increases when effects of a traumatic childhood are present in a dysfunctional family - trauma from abuse, sexual abuse, bullying, and other traumatic events in childhood. These individuals didn't have a secure attachment in early childhood, and as adults they don't have a strong sense of self or identity. They live in constant fear that people will abandon them.

Symptoms and signs of Borderline Personality include:

Self-harm – cutting
Intense unstable relationships
Fear of abandonment; includes rushing into relationships
Distorted self-image
Impulsive behaviors – spending sprees, reckless driving, unsafe sex, binge drinking or eating
Feeling of emptiness
Difficulty trusting others
Anger issues
Dissociating
Intense mood changes
Suicidal thoughts or threats

Borderline Personality relationships

Relationships take work, and some may need a little more work than others. If you're in a relationship with a Borderline, it's recommended you learn about this diagnosis to understand the additional stress it will add to the relationship. It is better to be educated, to spare both of you the heartache that would result from any hesitation to do the work of learning about it.

Relationships with a Borderline

Romantic relationships with a Borderline will have their own challenges because of the constant changes in the Borderline's emotions that their partner will endure. Borderlines tend to have chaotic relations both platonically and romantically. They tend to have a constant negative self-image and may engage in self-harm behaviors, have severe mood swings and make impulsive choices. The Borderline's fear of abandonment by their partners creates mistrust in the relationships and it takes a lot of work for their partners to believe their true love for them. Borderlines are hyper-sensitive to other people's moods and feelings - they can sense the subtlest change in others, which can lead to intense drama, and verbal as well as physical attacks. These relationships can cause the feeling of being suffocated and a perceived need to continuously be justifying themselves to the Borderline.

Several challenges in these relationships include:

Severe changes in self-image from worthy to worthless
Extremely affectionate and within hours the extreme opposite
Emotions and reactions can change daily
Black and white thinking/view of others
Impulsive, risky behavior, gambling, unprotected sex, drug, and alcohol abuse
Intense anger, anxiety, and depression
Episodes can last several hours or several days
Prone to accidents and threats of suicide are common
Difficulty seeing others' perspective
Overwhelming fear of abandonment and rejection
Self harm and attempts of suicide
Positive experiences may last several days just as bad experiences can also last several days

Easy, relaxed moments, though sparse, can be enjoyed, but the emotional rollercoaster can be trying as the littlest things can spiral their feelings. Because someone is Borderline it doesn't mean a relationship can't work. Education is an important factor in working with these relationships; they can be long-lasting. At the same time, a Borderline can be exceptionally caring and compassionate, and for a partner this can be reason to make the relationship work. Unfortunately, work and time may not always resolve these fears and without treatment it can escalate in intensity.

Relationships with a Borderline man

The signs of Borderline Personality Disorder (BPD) in men are not always the same as the signs in women. Men who are BPD won't always know it. Men with BPD are more likely to show a lot of anger than women with BPD. They are also more likely to be paranoid, passive aggressive, narcissistic and sadistic.

In early childhood males, BPD is often confused with:
Oppositional Defiant Disorder
Attention Deficit Disorder
Intermittent Explosive Disorder
Conduct Disorder
Bipolar Disorder

Men with BPD:

May express it through substance abuse or addictions to sex, shopping or gambling.

May date many women at the same time while refusing to commit to any of their partners out of fear of abandonment.

May scare their lovers away with aggressive behaviors, extreme jealousy, and quick tempers.

May begin to reject all relationships, including friendships.

Blame-shift feelings of failure, disapproval, guilt, and deficiency to other people they hold responsible.

May struggle to accept responsibility if they are at fault, not knowing how to cope with their feelings of guilt.

May be emotionally sensitive, perceiving most everything as personal attacks, and feeling criticized by any remarks made about them.

Many men are inclined to compensate for the lack of control they feel by attempting to control all of their adult relationships.

May make extreme threats to demonstrate their feelings, such as threatening a partner with an affair or actually acting out sexually with others to gain attention.

Some men may struggle to accept boundaries.

Men living with BPD tend to get different types of therapy treatment.

Recognizing patterns

In this section you are going to think about the relationships in your life and identify the people in your life with whom you may have a Borderline relationship. Read each red flag and think about one or more situations and how you feel (felt) when you are in the presence of this person and check off the appropriate box.

You can also write the names of these people and your relationship with them – partner, family, friend, co-worker – and reflect on a past or present situation, describing how you felt. Doing this exercise this will help you recognize behaviors and patterns. I've left space in the boxes for you to write about feelings, describe experiences, and note any patterns you begin to find.

Red flags in a Borderline relationship	Your partner	Family	Friend
Intense fear of abandonment			
Impulsive Behavior			
Unstable Relationships			
Self-Harm			
Rapid Changes in Self-Identity			
Mood Swings			
Chronic Feeling of Emptiness			
Intense Anger			
Paranoia and Loss with Reality			

Red flags in a Borderline relationship	Your partner	Family	Friend
Over-Sharing			
Dramatic			
Victimhood / Sympathy			
Obsession & Lack of Boundaries			
Splitting (Black and white thinking) - this is a defense mechanism where the person thinks in extremes (something is all good or all bad)			
Difficulty Regulating Emotion			
Numerous and frequent relationships, often close together			
Manipulating loved ones with suicide threats or attempts			

Self-care with a Borderline

Partners, family members and friends often feel exhausted by the Borderline in their life. Many people will express negative feelings towards them and feel embarrassed by their behavior. A person married to a Borderline has feelings of marital discord, humiliation and financial strain. Many people will avoid couple, family and friend gatherings because they don't know what to expect. Additionally, a Borderline will compete with their pattern of family, friends and coworkers and this leads to others not wanting to maintain the relationships. Borderlines will also triangulate people into an argument in order to gang up on a person. They pit one person against others, which is very destructive and drives people in their lives away.

How does someone cope and work with a Borderline? By setting clear and defined boundaries, effective communication and constant follow-through. Borderlines have a difficult time understanding other people's boundaries. They will push the limits, as they see boundaries as a form of rejection. It is up to you to stand your ground because it's so easy to fallen back into old patterns.

Make your mental health a priority – Your needs aren't selfish; they are important and needed to maintain normalcy and structure.
Have a talk about boundaries – Before setting boundaries, talk with the person and let them know what you need and why you need to set healthy boundaries.
Set boundaries – Determine what the boundaries are going to be. They must be clear. Think about your values and how these boundaries will protect you.
Decide the follow-up when boundaries aren't met – This is important because if the boundaries aren't respected, the boundaries established won't be taken seriously. The boundaries must be consistent.
Prepare for backlash – The Borderline can feel embarrassed and angry because of the boundaries that are in place. Then they will act out on you because this will be viewed as disrespect towards them.

Do not participate in the chaos.
Do not participate in the triangulation they create.

Eventually, the boundaries that are set forth must be consistent, and when they are challenged one must use the follow-up that was discussed with them. Follow-through is extremely important because over time they will understand what you set forth, and if they want to be in your life, they will respect the boundaries that were agreed by both parties. Yes, this can be viewed as forcing a Borderline to respect boundaries, because this is the only way they will respect them.

Key Differences and Similarities
between these Diagnoses

Differences:

Narcissistic Personality Disorder	Borderline Personality Disorder
Individual has a significantly inflated sense of self worth. They lack empathy, have an arrogant attitude, are envious, and exploit other individuals.	Individual exhibits reckless and impulsive behavior, unstable moods and relationships. Suffers BRIEF PSYCHOTIC mood swings.

Similarities:

The need for validation and attention
The word revolves around them
Will disconnect from reality
Will have unstable relationships
They disregard how their words and their actions affect others
Rigid thinking, all-or-nothing thinking
Feel a lot of shame
Easily sensitive to humiliation and criticism
Passive-aggressive and rageful

These personalities tend to be attracted to each other because they play out their own individual drama by fulfilling their own needs. Furthermore, a Narcissist can have borderline tendencies and a Borderline can have narcissistic tendencies.

Have you been (or are you) in a relationship with a narcissist? When did you recognize this? Are you still in the relationship, or have you left ?

Have you been (or are you) in a relationship with a borderline? When did you recognize this? Are you still in the relationship, or have you left ?

"Sometimes we're tested not to show our weakness but to discover our strengths."
--Suhani Jain

Before you begin the next section, I want to cover some common effects on children who grow up in Narcissistic and Borderline homes. This will help you learn more about *you* before you begin to reflect and have a better understanding of your life, choices, feelings, and behaviors that developed in your childhood.

Relationships with our parents are among the most special and strongest bonds we have in our lives. Children who grow up in narcissistic and/or borderline homes are faced with some similar and and some different challenges in childhood that could affect their lives in adulthood.

Your own attachment styles are influenced by how loving and caring your parents are. Without a healthy attachment in childhood, there is a tendency to create an emotional mess in adulthood which affects adult relationships. Unfortunately, and unconsciously, these children seek out relationships as adults that are toxic in nature, whether romantically or professionally. Thus, the children of a toxic childhood continue the loop of toxicity, manipulation and suffering with their own children.

Growing up with a Narcissistic parent (or parents)

Children of narcissistic parents can experience growing up with poor self-esteem because of the parent's possessiveness over their child's developing independence. Being raised in a home with a narcissist can take a mental toll on a child's mental health, and those children can develop traits of a narcissistic personality.

Children are likely to be insecurely attached to their parents because of a lack of trust in them. A child experiences neglect and manipulation from a narcissistic parent, and this leads to trust issues in adulthood.

Common traits of a parent with Narcissistic Personality Disorder include:

- **Live through their child's life.** The parent's expectation of their child is a fulfillment for their own selfish needs and dreams.
- **Marginalize their children.** A parent may feel threatened by their child and challenge their children by putting them down, judging them, criticizing them, comparing them, and diminishing a child's success so the parent can be superior to their child.
- **Grandiose image of themself.** A parent views their children as an object, not as human beings, because of the narcissistic parent's inflated sense of self.
- **Showing off.** Narcissistic parents enjoy showing off how special they are by flaunting their appearance, possessions, accomplishments, and even their children.
- **Manipulation.** Narcissistic parents manipulate their children with:
  Blaming – it's the child's fault when a parent isn't happy
  Guilt – when a child is made to feel they are ungrateful
  Shame – when a child does something that isn't perfect, it's an embarrassment
  Emotional coercion/pressure – pressuring a child to do their best so the parent is proud of them. Telling the child they need to do as the parent wants or they aren't good enough
  Reward and punishment
  Comparing them to other kids
- **Rigidity.** Narcissistic parents are rigid and can't stand when a child's behavior doesn't meet their expectations
- **Lack of empathy.** Narcissistic parents don't have the ability to be empathetic towards their children's thoughts and feelings or to validate them. It only matters what the parent thinks and feels.
- **Dependency.** Narcissistic parents expect their children to take care of them and depend on their children to provide for them emotionally, financially and/or physically. This expectation is expressed through manipulation, not in a healthy way that children would take care of their parents.
- **Jealousy.** Narcissistic parents may be jealous of their child's success, independence, maturity, career and appearance. A parent will guilt a child into feeling that they are hurting them and/or don't care for them because they aren't prioritizing the parent.
- **Neglect.** Narcissistic parent may neglect their children. The parent may focus on their own life and not be part of their child's. The parent may focus on their career, interest, and social life to the exclusion of their child's life and interests.

Effects narcissistic mothers have on their children

The narcissistic mother is all about *her* and believes she is entitled to that. She is incredibly self-absorbed. A narcissistic mother may feel entitled or self-important, believes she is above others, exploits her children, puts others down, experiences hypersensitivity to criticism, believes she deserves special treatment, and worst of all, may be naive to the damage she is causing.

A narcissistic mother:

Thinks it's one rule for her and another rule for everyone else
Doesn't respect her children's boundaries
Lacks empathy (or seems to turn empathy on & off)
Seemingly competes with her children
Gaslights her children
Only treats her children well in public
Often presents as the victim
Takes advantage of others

She is in petty rivalry with her own children. If a child outshines their mother in her talents or appearances, she will become jealous and find ways to put them down or destroy them. Mom will gaslight her children to a point they no longer trust themselves and become dependent on her version of reality.

Children will be told they are too sensitive, crazy, or some other derogatory name.

It is common for a narcissistic mother to give her children damaged gifts, to teach them they are unworthy and damaged. By doing this, a child is trained to think the damage must have been an accident because their mother would never do that - meanwhile, the mother enjoys seeing the child squirm and be nice to her.

Mothers sometimes train their children to play ill (Emotional Münchausen by proxy) in the form of fears, or even making them hurt themselves. To do this, the mother gives the child attention when the child fills this role. This teaches a child they are weak and not worthy, which sadistically makes the mother feel more powerful and needed.

The narcissistic mother treats her children as an extension of herself - her child is not their own person. The child becomes her trophy, and when they do well it's a reflection of her work in raising them. She'll never stop bringing it back to it being all about her, plus she will dramatize it all.
As long as the child aligns with what makes mother proud, they are good, and if it doesn't align it's not accepted.

She plays children against one another. When a narcissistic mother elects a "golden child" who can do no wrong, she also creates a scapegoat child and sometimes a child who's neglected. She will triangulate children against one another, keeping everyone in their place, teaching them that they need to work for attention or that they don't deserve it at all. Some mothers rotate those roles among their children, or they might play their child against a cousin, family and/or friend.

Effects narcissistic fathers have on their daughters

Daughters don't realize their father's behavior was abusive until well after it has had a toxic effect. By the time she understands there was something wrong with her father, the damage has already been done.

Narcissistic fathers:

Invalidate their daughters
Use triangulation to control them
Withdraw their love
Send a message to their daughter of "You're never enough"
Condition their daughters to interpersonal abuse
Rob their daughters of self-confidence
Cause their daughters to crave male attention
Undermine their daughter's developing sense of identity
Teach their daughters they don't have boundaries
Disregard their daughter's needs
Devalue their daughters
Exploit their daughter's talent
Teach their daughters learned helplessness
Value external beauty
Create codependent relationships

Effects narcissistic fathers have on their sons

Sons of narcissistic fathers are driven by lack of confidence, and they feel like they can never measure up or are enough to gain their father's approval. Their father may be critical and controlling and may belittle and shame their son's mistakes, vulnerability, and failures, and yet brag about him to his friends. A narcissistic father may bully or compete with his son in games and activities. Similarly, the father may be jealous of his wife's attention to their son and compete with him, and flirt with his girlfriends or wife.

As an adult, a son may have issues with:

Authority
Not managing anger well ("anger issues")
Passive aggressive behaviors
Suffering from shame
Suffering from anxiety
Poor self esteem
Suffering from codependency
Feeling unworthy of love
Finding partners who are emotionally unavailable
Lack of emotional closeness
Loneliness
Being driven to validate their self worth
Constant pressure to look perfect

Effects of being raised by a Borderline parent

Children who have one or more parents with Borderline usually experience a chaotic and abusive childhood. Many children feel like they are always walking on eggshells because they can't predict their parent's mood(s).

The effects of this in early childhood affect the child's attachment style. These children tend to have insecure attachment because parents with BPD miss the emotional and physical signs in their children. As a result of this, children grow up feeling unsafe, guarded, and/or needy.

Common traits of a parent with Borderline include:

- Seeking constant approval from their children and other family members
- Presenting as moody or depressed if things don't go their way
- Abusing drugs, alcohol, or other compulsive vices
- Self-harm and/or repeated suicide attempts
- A chronic pattern of unstable adult friendships or romantic relationships
- Rotating between extremes of "hating" and "loving" certain people
- Making kids feel like they need to "parent" their parent
- Making their children feel like they can never be "good enough" for their parent
- Lashing out with anger
- Ongoing fears of abandonment
- Paranoia and distrust toward other people

Children of Borderline parents are at heightened risk for:

Exhibiting attention difficulties
Aggressive behavior and low self-esteem
Major depression, anxiety, and Borderline Personality Disorder itself
Inability to trust their parents, tending to find it hard to trust others
Growing up feeling uncertain and ashamed of themselves
Poor relationship skills
Being so used to caregiving or people-pleasing that they fall into other relationships that mimic those patterns
Fear of being vulnerable with others, especially if they feel someone will use it against them

Hopefully, the last chapter was easily understood. Part of your work is going to be to read it over several times until you understand these diagnoses. Why? Because this is 80% of your healing, since both types exhaust people in different ways. Whether you feel loneliness, guilt, fear, abandonment, or depersonalization, the impact this toxicity has had on your life needs you to know *it's not you.* Easier said than done? Actually, it is - so you're going to stop telling yourself that it isn't. What you tell yourself is what you're going to get. Why would you continue negative self talk? I recommend you stop doing that and work on positive self talk. As you continue to do this, positive self talk will be the new norm for you.

People and things are possessions and presentations for them. Yes, it hurts to hear, but it's reality. If it doesn't fit their narrative, that narrative will be changed over and over until it does. **Accepting the diagnosis and eliminating the personalization is going to be the most challenging work for you.** I spend months helping families, partners, spouses, and children get to this point. Once they do, then their work starts to become attainable, and they are able to move ahead in life and focus on their continued healing, addressing their own pain so they can get to a healthier and happier self.

Another reminder – Narcissistic Personality Disorder and Borderline Personality Disorder are mental illnesses. The toxic person/people in your life may have traits of these diagnoses, but not have a mental illness; they can recognize the toxic behaviors and change.

In the remaining pages, you are going to redirect focus to *you*. You may not be thrilled when you get to the section about *Are you toxic?* Yes, it happens. If you grew up in a home, you've learned personality traits - now it's time to recognize, own and work through this. It's more common than not, and it's nothing to be ashamed of. You have the choice to want to change and you have the choice not to change. You decide this when you are ready.

Learning about you

We never excuse toxic or abusive behavior. We educate why people are abusers, why the abused stay, and what they learn from the abuser. Part of healing is learning and understanding how this happens, where it starts, and how to own your role – yes, recognize your role in a situation. This is not a fault or blame, this is to help someone recognize "How can I change what *I'm* doing, because what *you're* doing and how *you're* living isn't mentally healthy."

No one is perfect. We all make mistakes and deserve a chance to reflect on our actions, reactions and behaviors. We deserve the chance to make an effort to become better people and change unhealthy behaviors, actions, reactions, habits, and whatever else we want to work on.

The first part of your growth is to learn about your family. I know you know your family, but you are going to learn about them from a different perspective so you can recognize patterns and gain a better understanding of you. We are not going to fault anyone for who they are, because we are who we are for many reasons, and your goal is to learn so you can better help *you*. Doing a genogram is helpful because it's visualization, which is an effective way of helping us to recognize patterns we've never seen before.

Let's begin.

What is a Genogram?

A genogram is a representation of a family tree that displays details of relationships among members in the family. This visual representation is a powerful way to recognize patterns within a family and relationships. The detail contained in a genogram can vary from basic to extreme detail; the type of information is decided by the person working on the genogram and what they want to learn. Many people use genograms to better understand themselves, their relationships, and their life.

A person can design genograms for the following:

Relationship between all family members
Known diagnosis of each family member
Conflict among family members
Recognize behavior patterns
Patterns in their own relationships

You decide what you want to learn from this exercise. You can write as little as you want or as much as you need.

If you are unsure how to start, I've set up a generic genogram, a brief description of the relationship between family members, and a blank genogram for you to fill out - one for family and one for general/intimate relationships.

Additionally, you can look online for alternative templates and other explanations.

Family Genogram

Symbols

⬭ Female

▢ Male

X   Deceased
+++ Committed relationship
+-+- Separated
***   No contact - Broken relationship

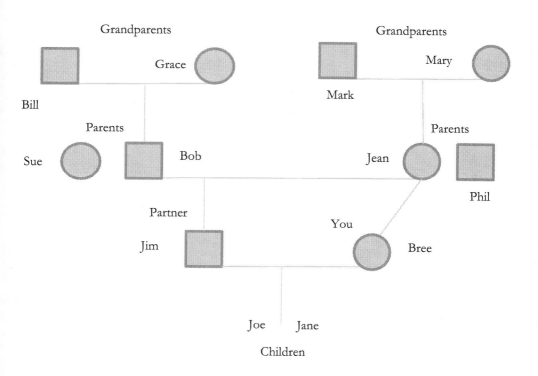

Example of information you can use for your genogram.

Bree and Jim

Married 21 years
Two kids
Jim is a banker
Bree is a stay-at-home mom. Bree takes care of the home and children
Relationship has defined roles
Jim is a perfectionist, rigid in his thinking and materialistic.
The marriage has had problems for the last 4 years. Jim is verbally abusive to Bree.
Bree feels stressed most of the time because she worries about what Jim complains about.
Bree's social life is small and when she goes out it's usually during the day while Jim is at work.

Bree's parents – Jean and Phil
Bree has a strained relationship with her mother, Jean. Jean is very controlling, manipulating, and has very little empathy.
Bree's relationship with her father, Phil, is loving. Phil is very caring – a people pleaser.

Jean and Phil's relationship is dominated by Jean. Jean's mood fluctuates and outbursts towards Phil are common.

Bree's grandparents – Mark and Mary
Mark has anger issues and is rigid. Mark is always right and everyone else is always wrong. Mary is always walking on eggshells with Mark.

Jim's parents – Bob and Sue
Jim doesn't speak to his parents because of his relationship with his mother. Sue is controlling, verbally abusive and only cares about their needs. Bob is verbally abusive and always negative.

Family Genogram

Symbols

◯ Female

▨ Male

X   Deceased
+++ Committed relationship
+-+- Separated
***   No contact - Broken relationship

Genogram

Symbols

⬭ Female

▭ Male

X   Deceased
+++Committed relationship
+-+- Separated
*** No contact - Broken relationship

What I learned from my Genogram:

What is Trauma?

What is trauma? A distressing experience or event that can impact a person's ability to function and cope that can result in psychological and emotional harm.

During a traumatic event, our thoughts can become scattered and disorganized in such a way that we no longer recognize those memories as belonging to us. Fragments of the memory are stored in our unconscious and later in life can become activated by anything closely reminiscent of the original traumatic experience. Once this is triggered it causes us to reenact the original trauma in our everyday lives.

Common traumatic experiences include:
Abuse (including domestic violence)
Death of a loved one
Assault
Rape
Job loss
Divorce
Violence
Accident
Illness
Prison

Some of us will get through life's difficulties unscathed, but for some of us a traumatic event can cause great suffering. There are many different types of traumas, which can be caused verbally, emotionally, physically and by bullying. Traumatic events can be intense and severe, and each person reacts to trauma in a unique way. Events that are traumatic to one person may not be to another person. Sometimes a parent's trauma can influence the stress patterns of their children, and these become the children's own trauma. This is known as passing generational trauma onto the next. Additionally, anxiety, stress and depression are passed on – so how do we break the cycle? Through healing yourself.

Most people are aware of their problems, but the approach used to resolve their concerns doesn't always work and they can't understand why their life isn't changing. When this occurs it's usually that the focus hasn't been about them, it's been on the other person. Before you can work on yourself, you will need to understand your family and childhood and put your past in the past in order to fully move forward. Trauma experienced affects so many things we do and how we live, although the trauma comes from a place of fear rather than authenticity. Trauma drives a person to mentally protect themself from going through past experiences and to take extra caution with people, careers, relationships and situations. Overcoming trauma involves recognizing where the trauma came from, sharing your experience with others and giving yourself time to heal. On the next page you will find common reactions from people when trauma has affected their life.

Effects of trauma

The effects of trauma can make it a struggle to regulate emotions, manage behaviors, plan day-to-day tasks and explore life.

Trauma can cause:

- Emotional numbing – this helps a person guard their feeling of what has happened and protects them from their deep feelings of the trauma.
- Gaslighting – this can lead to self-blame and doubt and minimize the trauma, resulting in thinking that you are crazy for your thoughts and feelings.
- Being out of touch with your emotions – a person can recognize their emotions, but they ignore them and will distance themselves from the experience that has/is occurring.
- Hypervigilance – a person will be attuned (increased alertness) to other people's emotions, which can lead to questioning people's feelings and emotions about you.
- Uncertain future – people will live with a sense they won't live long, and a fear of the uncertain amount of time they have left to live.
- Avoid conflict – a person can be reactive to arguments and feel their opinions don't matter, which causes them to shut down.
- Childhood memories – a person has difficulty remembering their childhood; they may block emotions, feelings and memories.
- Withdrawal – a person will isolate themselves from others; they feel detached and disconnected.
- Bottled up feelings – a person will create a defense layer for their hurt and pain and bottle all this up.
- Anxiety – a person will feel they will always need to be alert, which increases their anxiety.
- Highly critical of yourself – a person is extremely critical of themselves and can't get this criticism out of their thoughts.
- Trusting others – a person may find it difficult to trust other people and may view people as being unsafe.
- Chronic physical ailments – people will experience physical pain, stress, trouble sleeping and lower immune functioning.
- **Attracted to toxic people – a person's trauma shows up in their relationships, friendships and partnerships. A person will gravitate towards an abusive individual without realizing it because they are familiar with the abuse, chaos, and manipulation.**

Are you able to list your traumatic memories? Describe the triggers, how you feel and how you work through this.

Unfortunately, when the trauma consisted of abuse, the cycle of abuse and patterns of repeated behaviors can lead to trauma bonding in relationships.

What is Trauma bonding?

Trauma bonding is a deep dysfunctional emotional attachment that develops in an abusive relationship. In these relationships, the abuser is able to control their partner (the abused) by using tactics that make the partner fearful to end the relationship. Trauma bonding is similar to "Stockholm Syndrome," which is the term given to the people who became attached to their capturers back in 1973 in a hostage situation in Sweden. These people were held hostage for several days, and after they were rescued some of the hostages bonded with the capturers. This back-and-forth between the abuser and their partner is the pattern of abuse and reinforces the emotional attachment. Trauma bonding occurs due to the way a person's brain handles the trauma when a person is in survival mode.. The combinations of abuse and positive reinforcement create the trauma bond between the abuser and the abused. The bond forms out of the need for attachments as survival and this is how the abused becomes dependent on the abuser. The relationship is like being in a relationship with a partner who is narcissistic. Trauma bonding occurs at any time in a relationship.

This type of relationship has three phases:
Attachment, Dependence, Abuse

Common tactics an abuser may use to control their partner:

Intimidation – saying or doing things that will instill fear
Isolation – cutting off their family and friends
Emotional abuse – gaslighting, manipulating, name-calling, humiliation, criticizing, making their partner doubt events and their sanity
Minimization – the abused feelings of their trauma is made light of and/or denied by the abuser and the abuser justifies the abuse as deserved
Decision making – the abuser makes all decisions for the abused
Financial abuse – finances are controlled by the abuser
Threats – the abuser makes threats of violence against loved ones or pets to coerce their pattern into doing what the abuser needs.

You are Trauma bonded if you have these feelings:

You have become isolated.
You believe it's all your fault.
You are unhappy with them but terrified to lose them.
You lie to family and friends about the abuse.
You are covering up and making excuses for their behaviors to others.
You believe if you are better, they will change.
You don't know who you are anymore.

Do you recognize signs of trauma bonding in relationships? When did you first notice these signs?

If you struggle with relationships, the cause can be the attachment style you developed in your childhood. The following will help you recognize your attachment style so you can work on undoing these unhealthy patterns and have happier, healthier relationships.

Attachment styles develop in early childhood and may cause struggles with relationships in later life. If you had a secure attachment during childhood, you would likely be confident, trusting and have a healthy ability to work on relationships. However, if there was no secure attachment, the effects of having difficulties in relationships continue into adulthood. People with attachment issues are particularly susceptible to toxic relationships because they are emotionally vulnerable, often have abandonment issues, and for various reasons explained in the next chapter.

Attachment Styles

What is insecure attachment? It is a pattern that causes a person to feel insecure about their relationships. Because of the insecurity they feel with people, they struggle in adult relationships. There are several attachment types, but we will identify the ones that are present in toxic relationships.

Anxious attachment is when a person has a hard time feeling secure in a relationship. This person is more prone to insecurities and jealousy in their relationships and has a higher risk for anxiety disorders. Women who experience this attachment and abuse during childhood tend to have difficulties later in life in their relationships. Relationships for a person with anxious attachment tend to be stressful, unstable, and negative.

This style develops in early childhood and has a lifelong impact on:
The ability to communicate emotions
The ability to work through conflict
The ability to form healthy expectations

Signs of anxious attachment in adulthood present as:
Having difficulty trusting others
Needing constant reassurance
Fear of abandonment
Low self-worth
Moody, impulsive and unpredictable
Overly sensitive
Overly emotional
Being dependent in relationships

Avoidant attachment is when a person finds difficulty with emotional intimacy and distances themselves in relationships. These people can be fun to be with, but letting you get into their emotions is difficult. They avoid closeness and intimacy when relationships get serious. When they feel the other person is getting close, they may break up with them and start to distance themselves from them.

Signs of avoidant attachment in adulthood present as:
Avoiding emotional closeness
Withdrawing in difficult situations
Emotions are suppressed
Suppressing negative life events
Withdrawing from uncomfortable conversations
Hyper-focused on their own needs
Difficulty when partners are deemed too needy and/or clingy

Fearful-avoidant attachment is the most extreme attachment style because these people struggle with wanting to love someone but fear this bonding with another person. This attachment consists of both anxious and avoidant styles. This attachment style is usually the result of abuse and trauma in childhood which can consist of emotional, verbal, sexual and or physical abuse.

Signs of fearful-avoidant attachment in adulthood present as:
Unpredictable relationship behaviors
Extreme fear of rejection
Aggressive behavior
Negative self-image and low self-esteem
Not feeling loveable
Anxious and or depressed

Dependent Personality Disorder is an anxiety disorder characterized by the inability of a person to be alone. People with dependent personality disorder tend to rely on others for advice, support, reassurance and comfort. People with codependent tendencies or Dependent Personality Disorder tend to be attracted to toxic people because of their characteristics and fear of abandonment.

These feelings occur most of the time with no specific trigger. The anxiety is difficult to control and is disproportionate to the fear. This diagnosis manifests extreme neediness, clinginess, and submissiveness, which allow the person to remain in unhealthy relationships. The person has difficulty making decisions and always requires advice and reassurance from others. The risk factors for this individual may have been contributed to by a history of neglect, an abusive childhood, relationship abuse, authoritarian parents, or a family history of anxiety.

Characteristics include:
- Avoidance of personal responsibilities
- Difficulty being alone
- Sense of helplessness and fear of abandonment
- Oversensitive to criticism
- Difficulty making everyday decisions
- Lacks self-confidence
- Can be naïve
- Fearful of rejection
- Hurt by disapproval

If you struggle with relationships, the cause can be the attachment style you developed in your childhood. The following questions will help you recognize your attachment style so you can work on undoing these unhealthy styles and have happier, healthier relationships.

Do you recognize signs of anxious attachment in yourself? When did you first notice these signs?

Do you recognize any signs of avoidant attachment in yourself? When did you first notice these signs?

"Do one thing every day that scares you."
--Eleanor Roosevelt

Do you recognize signs of fearful-avoidant attachment in yourself? When did you first notice these signs?

Do you recognize signs of dependent personality in yourself? When did you first notice these signs?

"Have patience. All things are difficult before they become easy."
--Saadi

Anxiety

Why mention Anxiety? Because if you are anxious, irrational thoughts are part of your thinking patterns and these unhealthy thinking patterns affect your quality of life. The irrational thoughts impact relationships, and when there is a toxic person in your life, your anxiety will be on high alert.

So, what is Anxiety?
An emotion characterized by feelings of fear, tension and worry. It is a reaction to stress. It is excessive worry and fear usually about everyday situations, an event, or something with an uncertain outcome. The feelings are extreme and interfere with your daily life.

What is the difference between normal anxiety and an anxiety disorder?

- **Normal anxiety**: Individuals experience anxiety as a reaction to an event or situation that occurs in their life and usually lasts for a short period of time. This anxiety does not affect their quality of life.
- **Anxiety disorder**: Recurring intrusive thoughts and/or concerns that do not go away. The fear and worry are present all the time, which can increase in intensity and frequency and affect one's quality of life. This anxiety becomes overwhelming and surfaces for no reason. You may also find yourself avoiding situations out of worry.

Why am I anxious?
- Genetics
- Brain chemistry
- Personality
- Ongoing stressful events
- Influenced by environmental factors

What effects can anxiety disorders have?
Individuals can experience anxiety attacks, panic attacks, social isolation, depression, and challenging relationships, which challenge a person's ability to work and perform routine activities.

Generalized Anxiety Disorder is when an individual has excessive worry about events or activities, e.g., family, school, friends, work. These feelings occur most of the time with no specific trigger. This anxiety is difficult to control and is disproportionate to the fear.

Common symptoms include:

- Sleep disturbance
- Irritability
- Difficulty concentrating
- Muscle tension
- Weak or tired
- Sense of danger
- Increased heart rate
- Sweating
- Restlessness
- Chronic headaches

It's time to learn about your anxiety. Upsetting events don't happen as often as you think, but when they do, they can be because people feel afraid, upset, uncertain, and helpless. There are different kinds of upsetting/confusing events. Let's learn about the anxiety-inducing events that you experience. Here you're going to recall anxious moments (unsettling events/situations when you became anxious) and answer the following questions:

List your symptoms:

When does it happen?

Why does it happen?

How often does it happen?

How do you feel when it happens?

How do you handle the situation?

Are you living in the past? How? Why?

How often are you predicting the future? Why?

Do you really want to change? Yes, it's a question. Why? Because sometimes people are so comfortable with what they know, that they are afraid to change because they can't imagine what it would be like to feel better. Well, decide if you want change – and do it.

"Begin anywhere."
--John Cage

Core Beliefs

What are core beliefs?
Negative core beliefs are beliefs (assumptions/expectations) we think about ourselves (our identity), others, and the world. These beliefs are our security, insecurity, self doubt, and validation of ourselves. They are also assumptions that influence our behavior, how we see others and situations.

Why do I think this way?
These beliefs can start in childhood, early adulthood, and from traumatic experiences. They are learned from experience. Negative beliefs about yourself can stem from early childhood criticism from others, including high expectations from others. Negative core beliefs of others usually develop from witnessing or experiencing traumatic experiences and relating these experiences to the world.

How do negative core beliefs affect me?
Negative core beliefs can impact feelings, behaviors, and our perception of how we should be and expect others to be. **These beliefs can lead a person to negative self talk that can lead to cognitive distortions, which is irrational thinking.**

Can I change my negative core beliefs?
Yes, it is possible to change the negative beliefs. It will take work and can be challenging because these beliefs are embedded and formed in early life. You will need to recognize your patterns to determine the negative core beliefs.

Are core beliefs and expectations similar?
Yes, when we project our negative core beliefs onto others, we are expecting them to think and feel them the same way we do, and when they don't it creates a disconnect between us.

What are unhealthy core beliefs?
A person's unhealthy core belief is a negative automatic assumption about themselves and others:

I am a loser	No one likes me	I am worthless
I am no good	I am bad	I am unlovable
I can't do anything right	I am not smart	I am ugly
I am weak	I will be lonely	Nothing is ever easy
I am a failure	I don't belong	I am always doing something wrong
I cannot trust	I am not in control	I am inadequate
I can't trust myself	It's not right to show emotion	I will be alone
I do things wrong	I should know better	

I am not thin; therefore no one thinks I'm pretty.
If I don't meet others' expectations, I am not a good person.
I am not rich; therefore, I am not successful.
I am not smart and can't do anything.
People who don't agree with me are difficult and not nice.
People who don't work hard are lazy.
If I don't do well in school, I will never succeed.
If someone doesn't call me back that means they don't like me.

What are healthy core beliefs?

I am a good person	I am lovable	I deserve to be happy
I learned from the situation	I can express myself	I am in control
I can trust people I want to trust	I am worthwhile	I can make mistakes
I did my best	I have courage	I choose to be positive
I am good with who I am	I am important	I trust my choices

What else can negative core beliefs do to me?

A person may find it difficult to trust other people; may be aggressive; may, without realizing it, always put their needs on the back burner and take care of others; may feel inadequate in relationships; and can be very confrontational.

Can you give an example of a negative core belief and what the positive belief could be?

Negative

June: "I am always a failure."
Situation: Believes she is a failure because she forgot to complete a project on time
Feeling: Is depressed
Behavior: Her depression stops her from making any changes to her negative belief

Bob: "I have no luck."
Situation: Bob didn't get a job he interviewed for and feels he has no luck
Feeling: Is depressed
Behavior: His depression stops him from making changes to his negative belief

Positive

June: "I try my best."
Situation: June didn't get enough sleep and couldn't concentrate
Feeling: Disappointed
Behavior: Won't stay up late when projects are due

Bob: "I trust my choices."
Situation: Bob applied for a job that he did not qualify for
Feeling: Disappointed
Behavior: Will learn from the situation and stay focused

Core beliefs and anxiety

The following situation is an example you can use to help you with recognizing your core beliefs and how they trigger your anxiety.

Situation: Bill's wife Debra tells him she feels that he doesn't love her the same way as she does and needs him to express it to her more. She tells him he doesn't say it enough and feels alone and hurt. Bill responds to Debra and tells her that he does not need to always tell her. Debra replies, "I don't believe you," and the conversation turns into an argument.

Debra's core belief   If I don't express my emotions, it means I am not lovable

↓

Debra's expectation: People need to validate their love to feel loved

↓

Irrational Thought: Fortunetelling, catastrophizing, all-or-nothing thinking

↓

Anxiety Trigger: Bill doesn't tell Debra he loves her on a regular basis. His beliefs are different than Debra's and because of this her anxiety was triggered.

List your negative core beliefs:

Think back and explore when each belief originated:

Replace the negative core beliefs with positive core beliefs.

"A positive mind looks for ways it can be done; A negative mind looks for ways it can't be done."
--Napoleon Hill

Irrational Thinking

What is irrational thinking?
Irrational thoughts or beliefs are distorted perceptions of reality that present in a negative way and occur under emotional distress. These thoughts are emotional reactions to situations.

Can these thoughts affect your life?
Yes. They will increase anxiety, depression and stress.

Does everyone have irrational thought patterns?
Yes, we all do, but someone with an anxiety disorder struggles with looking at a situation logically and continues to think the worst. Most people with anxiety have irrational thought patterns. They are aware of this but can't control their thoughts. There are also times these thoughts are automatic, a habit.

How do I determine if my thought patterns are affecting my quality of life and making me anxious?
To help determine if thought patterns are affecting your quality of life, ask yourself the following questions:

How often do you find fault in everyone else? Is it almost all the time, or just some of the time? If it's almost all the time, it is likely affecting your quality of life. Now, ask yourself how it can be *all of the time?* Is everyone else always wrong? Do people always wrong you?

The goal is to recognize your irrational thinking patterns and to remind yourself when your thoughts are irrational. "Why am I thinking this way? What do I gain by thinking this way? How do I feel when I think this way?" How about your expectations and assumptions? These also play a large role in anxiety. Once you begin to recognize your irrational thoughts, you will start to think in a healthier way, and you are on your way to a calmer self.

How can I can make this work for me?
By working at it, recognizing your patterns, and committing to changing the thought pattern(s) when you are ready.

On the next page, you will find common irrational thinking patterns. After you have read each one, determine those that apply to you. Check them off and date the bottom of the page. Your goal is to recognize irrational thinking patterns and to replace them with healthier ones. Occasionally, revisit the irrational thinking checklist to see how far you have come. It's great to see the progress you are making.

Common Irrational Thinking Patterns

After reading the thought patterns, check off the one(s) that you do most or all of the time. Once you have completed this, the next step is to raise awareness so you can recognize when it occurs. You will learn to automatically recognize when the irrational thought is occurring and eventually challenge the thought.

❑   **All-or-nothing thinking:** An individual views everything in the extreme. It's either right or wrong, true or untrue. Rarely does one see shades of grey. This is the inability to see alternatives to a problem.

❑   **Overgeneralization:** An individual takes one experience and believes this will always occur. For example, you're not invited to a party, therefore you'll never be invited to any parties.

❑   **Catastrophizing or minimizing:** An individual either exaggerates or minimizes a situation. For example:

Catastrophizing: Billy bumped into another student during lunch and the student's apple fell on the floor. The student told Billy it was okay and that it was just an accident, but Billy got so upset over it that he thought about it for days.

Minimizing: Mary beat the track record at school and won an award. Afterward, she gave a short speech and people applauded her. However, Mary complained that she was so nervous that her speech was dumb.

❑   **Emotional reasoning:** An individual views that how they feel is what defines them. For example, Jane feels dumb, so she's convinced that she is dumb, even though she does well in school.

❑   **"Should" statement:** This statement (also includes "ought" or "must") usually induces feelings of guilt; the motivation for doing something is based on what others think. This thinking usually leads to procrastination.

Common Irrational Thinking Patterns

❑ **Labeling and mislabeling:** An individual does the opposite of overgeneralization.
Labeling - you label yourself: "I'm dumb."
Mislabeling - you label someone else's behavior: "She's a weirdo."

❑ **Personalization:** An individual believes they're the cause of a negative event. For example, if Mary doesn't call you back, she must not like you.

❑ **Fortune-telling:** An individual tends to predict that things will turn out badly.

❑ **Disqualifying the positives:** An individual doesn't give themselves credit when they do something positive and/or good. They feel it's not deserved.

❑ **Negative thoughts:** An individual only looks at the negative side of an event, situation, or action. For example, you lost your lunch money, but you had a great day with friends. Your focus is on the lost money.

Notes:

_____

_____

_____

_____

_____

_____

_____

_____

_____

_____

_____

"When one door of happiness closes, another opens, but often we look so long at the closed door that we do not see the one that has been opened for us."
--Helen Keller

What irrational thinking/behavior looks like:

Thoughts affect both your feelings and your body sensations, which, in turn, affect your overall behavior towards situations.

For example, thinking, "nobody likes me" can create a feeling of anxiety (feelings) around other people, which, in turn, may cause sweaty palms (bodily sensations) resulting in withdrawing from your friends (behavior), resulting in feeling left out.

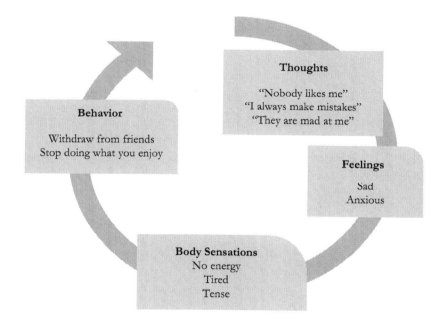

Your thoughts

We sometimes think about negative things over and over again – this is unhealthy thinking. You can stop this by *recognizing* when you're repeating the negative thinking in your head.

List all the negative thoughts you repeat over and over. Recognize your patterns.

How often do you find yourself stuck in these thought patterns? How often do you recognize the thought patterns that are occurring? Do you ruminate/overthink?

"Don't be pushed by your problems. Be led by your dreams."
--Ralph Waldo Emerson

Methods

When you find yourself overthinking, anxious, fearful, worried and stressed over situations (of course, not dangerous situations), try the following methods and determine the one that works for you.

Thought-stopping: Use your watch or phone when this is occurring.

Set a timer for 20 minutes and tell yourself you are not going to worry, stress, wonder, or overthink for the next 20 minutes. Find something to do for the next 20 minutes. Once the timer goes off, allow yourself to go back to your "worry" and think about what was going on in your thoughts. Ask yourself the following:

What value did the irrational thought add to my quality of life?
What benefit did the irrational thought bring to my quality of life?

Open the door: Visual

Visualize a door. Open the door. Put your situation outside the door, and then close the door.
Set a timer for 20 minutes and tell yourself you are not going to worry, stress, wonder, or overthink for the next 20 minutes. Find something to do for the next 20 minutes. Once the timer goes off, allow yourself to go back to your "worry" and think about what was going on in your thoughts. Ask yourself the following:

What value did the irrational thought add to my quality of life?
What benefit did the irrational thought bring to my quality of life?

Name your anxiety:

Yes, name your anxiety. Think of a fun name and talk to your anxiety when you're feeling anxious. Ex: "Welcome back, Dory. I know you're anxious, and I know what is going on in your thoughts. You're scared, your stomach is uneasy, and your negative thoughts are extreme. I know this happens and I know you're not logical at the moment. I know you always get past this. I also know that as I challenge you this will get easier."

This method allows you to accept and embrace your anxiety. It is part of you. The more often you fight your anxiety and find fault with it, you actually increase your anxiety. It is more challenging to reduce the intensity and frequency of when it occurs. Let your anxiety be your friend – really, it works.

Visualize your emotion/feeling:

Your negative emotions/feelings are a temporary state of mind. You will learn how to visualize your emotions/feelings. First, you will accept your emotions/feelings. Second, you are going to visualize your emotions as a concrete/physical object and picture it in front of you.

Answer the following questions while you imagine your emotion/feelings. What emotions/feelings affect your quality of life negatively? Name your emotion.

What color is it?

How big/what size is it?

How much does it weigh?

What does the texture feel like?

Does it have a smell?

Does it have a sound?

Now let us make it a physical object – find an object and place it next to you/in front of you.

Imagine your emotion as a physical object outside your body – you will now manipulate your emotion. Make the emotion exist outside of your internal self. As you start to recognize it as an object outside of you, you eventually will not identify the emotion the same way. Slowly, the emotion will not define you.

Example:

You have a chair you hate. This chair makes you feel frustrated. You have several solutions for the chair, so you do not need to feel frustrated and let it impact your mood. A few options may be to:

Move it outside

Donate it

Throw it away

Cover it up

All these solutions can physically change how you feel because you can see it, touch it, feel it, and do something about the chair. Once you do something about the chair, you are no longer frustrated. You have control of your emotions because the chair is a physical object you can do something about. Completing the exercise above allows you to teach your thought process to directly go to your emotion as an object and remove it from within.

What is your Emotional Scale?

Here you are going to gauge your emotional scale. We are unique, and each scale rating works differently when it relates to how we react to a situation. Some of us may overreact because of our irrational thoughts. When this occurs, we become very anxious and the situation escalates to misunderstanding, conflict, arguments and disappointments. Think of a situation and rate your anxiety using the scale. Once you have determined your average number, you can challenge your number by asking yourself: Does my anxiety warrant the situation? Are my irrational thoughts the core of the anxiety?

Once you determine your number, you can recall this number when you find your anxiety affecting the situation and challenge the irrational thoughts.

First, determine what the numbers mean to you.

Emotional Scale

1	2	3	4	5

1. Calm, no impact
2. Thinking about the situation; minimal reaction
3. Situation has elevated; you start to become defensive; tone gets louder, body language presents as guarded, angry, frustrated, anxious
4. Pissed off, angry, yelling, annoyed, anxious, frustrated; defensive mode
5. Reaction is over the top; heated, angry, yelling, frustrated; defensive mode, not listening to the other person.

Individuals who are anxious tend to function at 3-5 on the scale because of their irrational thought patterns. It is important to learn your thought patterns so you can use the scale to help you reduce your anxiety and eventually react in a healthier manner.

Always remember, whatever method you choose: Revisit the thoughts after you've had time to de-escalate. Your ability to evaluate and have clarity will help you continuously challenge the negative thoughts.

Expectations and Assumptions

What are expectations? *Expectations are the strong belief that something will happen or should be a certain way. More than anything else, our* **expectations** *determine our reality, and our* **expectations** *also impact those around us. In a self-fulfilling prophecy, we may rise or fall depending on our* **expectations** *and beliefs.*

Of course, we all have them, and at times we blame them for our disappointments, frustrations, and conflict. However, sometimes we need to sit and self-reflect what our expectations are. We need to revisit our core beliefs and either learn to be more flexible in our beliefs or lower the expectations of others to find a healthy balance.
It is also important for the people in our lives to know what your expectations are. Don't assume they know – they aren't you. Do we self-sabotage? Can we learn to be more flexible in understanding? Can we lower some of our expectations to avoid the disappointment when others don't meet them?

Expectations can come from our core beliefs and can be projected onto others. When they fail to meet our expectations, we have a problem. From our perspective we assume they don't care, they are not respectful, they don't appreciate us, they are hurtful, they are selfish, and whatever else we come up with. Sometimes these reasons are valid and sometimes they aren't. It's when they aren't true that creates tension, resentment, disappointment, anger and hurt. An easy solution is to recognize your expectations, as they can contribute to your anxiety.

Adjusting expectations:

Don't expect people to think like you.
Don't expect people to treat you how you want to be treated.
Don't expect people to know what you mean.
Don't expect people to believe the same as you do.

Additionally, how do you feel when you project your expections onto others:

Let down
Hurt
Angry
Disappointed
Misunderstood
Unheard
Unloved

In our lives, we all have titles, and with these titles come a role we try to fit into. Overall, society has created these titles and descriptions and we are expected to match our role to these titles.

Title	Description	Expectation to fit this role in society
Father	Provider, Caregiver Supporter of his children Devoted, Caring, Compassionate	To fit the social norm of being a good father to his children
Mother	Provider, Caregiver Supporter of her children Devoted, Caring, Compassionate	To fit the social norm of being a good mother to her children
Wife	Provide for her spouse, personal needs and home needs	To fit the social norm of being a good wife
Husband	Provide for his spouse financially	To fit the social norm of being a good husband
Sister	Caring, devoted	To fit the social norm of being a good child and sister
Brother	Caring, devoted	To fit the social norm of being a good child and brother

Now comes the downfall of expectations not being met. The titles don't always fit the "expected" roles of these individuals, so depending on one's core beliefs, it can be the perfect storm for conflict, disappointment, frustration, anger, and resentment. Why? Because the societal expectations have not been met. These expectations don't take mental health issues into account. The result can be that one family member then projects these expectations onto others because their own core beliefs don't allow them to align with the traditional roles.

"Whenever I hear someone sigh, 'Life is hard,'
I'm always tempted to ask, 'Compared to what?'"
--Sydney Harris

List your expectations of others:

Replace the high expectations with rational expectations:

"If people are doubting how far you can go, go so far that you can't hear them anymore."
--Michele Ruiz

Thought Diary

This exercise will help you think more rationally about an assumption and/or rule that may be harmful thinking.

Think about a scenario when you felt bad about your thought. Write a short description about the situation.

Next, identify the assumption/thought that occurred. How did you react?

Challenge yourself and ask yourself what happened in your life to acquire this thought, how/when did you learn it, and what encouraged you to believe it?

Once these questions are asked, you are going to compare the advantages and disadvantages of thinking this way.

Use self talk to stop the irrational thoughts. Make yourself aware of these irrational thoughts as they occur. Keeping a daily log can also be helpful. The following is an example to assist you in finding the method that works for you so you can learn to replace the unhealthy thoughts with healthier thoughts.

The situation	What negative thought did you have	Choose an alternative healthy thought
"I am so nervous speaking in public. I know people are thinking how awful I am presenting."	Focusing on the negative	"I am more confident and a better speaker than I realize. I've always done well, and people have told me this."
"I'll never feel content. I will always worry about everything."	Overgeneralizing	"I can be laid back and be relaxed. I can choose to let go of my worries."
"My stomachache must mean something is wrong with me."	Catastrophic thinking	"Many reasons my stomach can hurt. Most of the time it's my food choices and it goes away."
"If I can't be in control I can't function during the day."	Should	"I can only control my actions and reactions. I cannot control how other people react and act."

Advantages of your negative thought patterns:

_____

_____

_____

_____

Disadvantages of your negative thought patterns:

_____

_____

_____

_____

_____

Coping with your upsetting feelings:

When you experience an upsetting feeling, there are steps you can take to reduce the intensity. What are some things you do, and could do, to reduce the feelings?

What you do:

What you can do instead:

"You're so much stronger than your excuses."
--Unknown

How do you communicate?

Why is communication important? For starters, because it's an essential part of life – but learning how to communicate effectively takes work. The ability to communicate in an effective way is one of a person's most important skills. When communication is effective, we can understand our needs and have the ability to articulate them to the people in our lives. Of course, it takes other people to communicate effectively, and you will always be challenged by someone who isn't a good communicator – but that doesn't mean you can't continue to keep progressing in your communication style.

Not to worry; effective listening and communication are not always easy. There are many factors that go into miscommunication, including feeling shy, scared, or angry, all of which break down effective communication.

The inability to listen, and its associated complications, can also cause distress in family situations that would easily be handled if we knew how to better communicate with each other. Complications may include differences in learning styles, cultural differences, and psychological disorders.

By the way, if you are wondering why I've included this in the book – it's because it is important. Communication can decrease one's anxiety, and the other person will be able to hear and understand you better. Once you start conversations with the "I" statements, you will experience how healthy most conversations can be. Your thought patterns will be challenged when you communicate this way, and your defensiveness and over-explaining will slowly diminish because your confidence and self esteem will be stronger.

When in conflict, redirect the conversation back to the issue, because people will divert to keep the conflict and chaos going.

"Lack of communication ruins everything, because instead of knowing how the other person is feeling, we just assume."
--Unknown

Communication is effective when conversations go smoothly, and people understand the messages that were intended. However, this isn't always the case. Many times, wrong messages are heard, which leads to misunderstanding. So, what is ineffective communication? Many of us engage in shutting down and/or stopping people from expressing their needs. Why? Because we are either too emotional or we want to be heard first. The following are some reasons why communication fails:

Ignorance
Cultural diversity
Emotional
Distance (not face-to-face)
Digital (texting/phone))
Hierarchy

Additionally, there are many ways in which we engage in ineffective communication and shut down a conversation without realizing it.
Here are a few examples:

Ignoring you or pretending you don't hear
Blaming – using "you" too often is very aggressive, and this leads to everyone being defensive
Deflecting – a way to divert the attention away from a person's own actions, beliefs and feelings. This is a way to push the blame on the other person.
Blocking – when someone suddenly stops talking in the middle of a conversation.
Undermining – telling someone what they are saying isn't true/they are wrong – let the other person speak because this is their perception.

Examples of ineffective communication:

"I am busy, not right now."
"You always want to talk."
"You didn't call me before you left."
"You are always doing this."
"You are always running late."
"You never agree with me."

Examples of effective communication:

"I am busy, but I can talk after 2 pm."
"I would like to talk. Are you available?"
"Can you please call me before you leave work?"
"I would like to understand why you do that."
"I get upset when you are late."
"I feel unheard when we talk."
"I would like to work on our communication."

Healthy word choices and other ways you can communicate:

Learn to use "I" statements: *** Very important! It will change situations dramatically when you start off with "I".
"I am hurt when this happens." "I am unsure how to help you." "I want you to tell me what that feels like." "I want you to trust me." "I am here for you when you need me." "I don't understand, so help me understand." "I will listen to you." " I am unsure how to help you."

Minimize/Avoid "You" statements: "You" statements are a great way to start an argument and cause tension, putting the other person on the defense. Be very careful here. "You never listen when I tell you to do something." "You always forget." "You don't try hard enough." "You are always late."

Learn how to engage in active listening: Understand the information, including the words and emotions an individual is trying to communicate – it shows them you are interested and engaged. Provide positive feedback. Let them speak without interrupting.

Avoid blaming others.

Learn to use the 10 second rule: If you feel angry, let the other person know that you're going to take a 10 second break before you talk to them. If you're still angry, let the other person know you need a few minutes to gather your thoughts.

Learn how to validate feelings: Don't disqualify how you feel or how others feel. You are not them, and they are not you.

Write down a situation of conflict:

How did I communicate my feelings?

Do I recognize why I felt attacked?

"You can't go back and change the beginning, but you can start where you are and change the ending." --C.S. Lewis

Do I recognize a pattern that may cause the other person to feel attacked?

Did I approach the conversation with doubt?

How could I have communicated differently?

Was I flexible with understanding the perspective of the other person?

In the next chapter, boundaries are discussed because they set the guidelines of how you want people to treat you. I constantly remind my clients, we can always blame other people for disrespecting us, but in the end, *WE ALLOW PEOPLE TO TREAT AND TALK TO US THE WAY THEY DO* because of our lack of boundaries or not standing firm on our boundaries.

What are boundaries?

Boundaries are space between you and another person. One can use an imaginary line that separates two people from each other. This line keeps each person in their space, for their own feelings, needs and responsibilities, from the other person.

Boundaries are important because they allow you to have your own feelings, to ask for what you want and need without having to please others, and to make your own decisions. Without healthy boundaries, people can become enmeshed, which leads to the need to please others, which over time becomes mentally exhausting. Unhealthy boundaries lead to disrespect and disregard for your wants, values and needs, and in romantic relationships this increases to various types of abuse. Determining what healthy boundaries you require is a conversation to be had with the people in your life.

The strength of boundaries is an indicator of your personal strength. Your boundaries aren't limited to intimate relationships – they are essential with family, friends, co-workers and other people who are in your life. When a person has weak boundaries, they are prey to people who manipulate, because manipulators recognize this weakness. So how does one recognize if they have weak boundaries?

The following are some indicators a person has weak boundaries:

You have a difficult time saying no to people – you tend to overextend yourself by doing a lot of things you really didn't want to do.
You put more into your relationships – you put extra work into the relationship to maintain a healthy balance and are always working on ways to do this.
You are always solving everyone else problems – you spend a lot of time "fixing" everyone else's problems while enabling other people's reliance on you.
Your life has a lot of conflicts – people can detect you have weak boundaries and will attempt to bring conflict into your life that doesn't belong to you.
You are often disrespected – people know they can disrespect you because you lack boundaries.
Drama is part of your life – people who create drama will bring their drama to you.
You are easily guilted – people can get what they want and need from you because of weak boundaries.
You put other people's needs over your own – you prioritize other people's needs and happiness over yours.
Steps in setting effective boundaries consist of the following three components:
Setting the boundaries – Think about where you need to set boundaries. Identify the most important boundaries.
Implementing and communicating the boundaries – Think about the people you need to set the boundaries with and why you need to set these boundaries. Communicate with these people and let them know what boundaries you are setting and why.
Maintaining and managing the boundaries – Managing these boundaries will require follow-through. You will have to know what are you going to do when the boundaries are violated.
Once you have determined the boundaries, you need to decide what steps you're going to take to implement them.

Healthy Boundaries

So, what do healthy boundaries look like? What does that mean? For you to better understand, I've listed several examples:

Physical boundaries – This is your own personal space; consists of touch and physical needs.
- I am really tired. I am going to rest.
- I am a not a hugger. I'd rather shake hands.
- I don't want you to take my personal stuff without asking first.
- I am sorry the kids got to bed early, we'll have to make plans for another night.

Emotional boundaries – This is about respecting your feelings. This includes when you want to share or not share your emotional feelings with others. This validates your feelings to others.
- I am sorry you are having a difficult time. Right now, I'm not in a mental state to take all this in. Can you come back to revisit this conversation?
- I can't talk right now. This isn't the right time.
- When I share how I feel to you and get criticized, it makes me sad. I can only talk to you when you are respectful to me.

Examples of violating boundaries include:
- Criticizing and dismissing feelings
- Going through personal information without permission
- Sharing inappropriate feelings with your children
- Making assumptions you know how other people are feeling

Time boundaries – these include boundaries at work, home and socially. Without these boundaries, people tend to overcommit themselves, which leads to neglecting your priorities.
- We have date night on Saturdays, we can't make it.
- I can only stay for a half hour.
- I am more than happy to help you. My availability is from 12 – 2.
- I can't help you tomorrow.

Sexual boundaries – this includes understanding of consent, preferences, and respect.
- Asking for consent
- Talking about what pleases you
- Discussing protection
- Saying no, that is not comfortable for you

A violation of boundaries consists of:
- Pressure to engage in sex
- Not asking for consent
- Getting angry if you don't want to have sex
- Unwanted touch

Healthy Boundaries you want to implement:

	Partner	Family
Physical boundaries:		
Emotional boundaries:		
Time boundaries:		
Sexual boundaries:		

Healthy Boundaries you want to implement:

	Friend (s)	Coworker (s)
Physical boundaries:		
Emotional boundaries:		
Time boundaries:		
Sexual boundaries:		

Check In With Your Progress

Notes to self: What have I learned?

"The greatest weapon against stress is our ability to choose one thought over another."
--William James

What I can control and what I can't

I can control:

- ☐ **My boundaries**
- ☐ My thoughts and actions
- ☐ The goals I set
- ☐ What I give my energy to
- ☐ How I speak to myself
- ☐ How I love myself
- ☐ How I allow others to treat and speak to me
- ☐ How I value myself
- ☐ How I handle challenges
- ☐ Letting go of toxicity

I can not control:

- ☐ The past
- ☐ The actions of others
- ☐ The opinions of others
- ☐ What has happened to me
- ☐ The outcome of any effort I make
- ☐ How other people take care of themselves

Don't expect to be perfect: You are doing your best.

"6+3= 9 but so does 5+4. The way you do things isn't always the only way to do them. Respect other people's way of thinking."
--Unknown

Do I have toxic traits?

There are always aspects of yourself that you can improve, and it's inevitable that your own toxic traits – yes, you read correctly – may impact your life. Being honest with yourself is important and having awareness of how other people view you and how you view yourself will help you recognize any toxic traits you may have. We don't always realize our own toxic traits and sometimes we spend a lot of time looking at and blaming others. However, it takes looking inward to own our role and recognize how we are affecting our everyday lives. Some people are more susceptible to toxic qualities based on their personality, diagnosis, and life experiences. We can always improve on ourselves by learning to recognize the areas we need to improve, and this comes with self-awareness. It relates to how we see our behaviors, values, thoughts, strengths, and weaknesses and recognize how we impact the people in our lives; being honest with ourselves. So, take a pause and reflect on your own traits and take action to improve your mental health and improve your quality of life.

On the next few pages, you are going to explore whether you have any unhealthy behaviors and toxic qualities, and if so, to what degree.

Unhealthy behaviors

- ❏ Judgmental – judge people and situations without experiencing
- ❏ Dishonest – lie, mislead others
- ❏ Negative – complain and put a damper on most experiences, people
- ❏ Rude – not having manners towards others
- ❏ Bossy – having control and dominance in situations
- ❏ Greedy – taking more at the expense of others
- ❏ Inconsistent – not following through with commitments, family, friends, work
- ❏ Sneaky – not honest with your actions for your benefit
- ❏ Lack of empathy – not recognizing other people's feelings
- ❏ Not taking responsibility – avoiding responsibility and not apologizing when you know you were wrong
- ❏ Thoughtless – you don't take other people's feelings into consideration
- ❏ Self centered – you only focus on your own wants and needs

Recognizing your patterns
Narcissistic traits

	You
Have people ever told me they feel like they have to walk on eggshells around me?	
Are conversations always about me?	
Have I lost my values?	
I make fun of others	
I am in constant drama	
I don't respect people's boundaries	
I am self absorbed	
I am jealous of other people's accomplishments	
I expect people to respect me	
My self is worth more than others	
I keep score with people	

Recognizing your patterns
Narcissistic traits

	You
I blame other people for almost everything	
I expect my emotional needs to be taken care of first	
I lack responsibility	
I always have to speak my mind	
I expect defined roles	
I expect people to agree with me	
I am grandiose	
I deceive people	
I am dominating	
I gaslight others	
I manipulate people	
I lash out on people who don't agree with me	
I justify my bad behavior	

Time to reflect: What did I learn from the exercise on the previous page?

"Not all storms come to disrupt your life. Some come to clear your path."
--Unknown

Red flags you recognize about yourself
Borderline traits

	Yes	No
I have intense fear of abandonment		
I have impulsive behavior		
I have unstable relationships		
I self-harm		
I have rapid changes in self-identity		
I have mood swings		
I have chronic feeling of emptiness		
I have intense anger		
I experience paranoia and loss with reality		
I am always over-sharing		
I am always dramatic		
I present victimhood and look for sympathy most of the time		
I present obsession & disrespect boundaries of others		
I often split – this is a defense mechanism when people see events or themselves in black and white thinking		
I have extreme difficulty regulating my emotions		
I have numerous and frequent relationships, often close together		
I manipulate loved ones with suicide threats or attempts.		

Time to reflect: What did I learn from the exercise on the previous page?

"You're so much stronger than your excuses."
--Unknown

What's next?

Now that you have recognized any unhealthy behaviors and/or toxic tendencies, your next step is to work on changing this. How do you start?

Have a conversation with yourself and the important people in your life and ask them how you hurt them. This is going to be extremely difficult, and you may feel you need to defend yourself. Assure these people that they are safe to express themselves to you and let them know you want to work on being a better person and have a healthier relationship. Once they have expressed this to you, reflect on it, take a little time, and let them know how you are going to work on changing these behaviors.

Once you've taken all this information in and recognized your behaviors, it's time to address them. Start to make the change and be accountable to yourself. So, what do you do with all this information? Work on yourself. Start therapy (find a different therapist if needed), read books, and join groups that address self-exploration, hurt, anger, and/or boundaries.

Finding your peace

- You are allowed to terminate toxic relationships; you are allowed to walk away from those that hurt you; you are allowed to be angry and be unforgiving. You don't owe anyone an explanation for taking care of yourself.
- You are not obligated to forgive your abuser; you don't owe them anything. This is not an act of aggression, it's an act of peace.
- People don't abandon people they love. People abandon people they are using.
- Sometimes the closure you need is moving forward. They said everything to you with their actions.
- I release you with a full heart and take back all my energy and power I gave you.
- This new chapter in my life is called *my turn* and I'm going to be in control.

Breaking up with toxicity

Dear Me,

Breaking up with all the toxicity in my life will have its challenges. I understand these relationships drained me emotionally and the healing process doesn't have a deadline. Some days and weeks will be difficult, and some will be easier. I have to be kind to myself and know I will become stronger, find happiness, hope and contentment. I won't blame myself for not recognizing what happened to me – I will look back and it will be a far memory of the past. I could have never known this person was hurting me until the signs became so apparent, I stopped making excuses for their behavior. I will get through the stages of grief. I will practice self-care, exercise, socialize with friends and family, and participate in activities. I will also reflect and work through the denial, hurt and anger I experienced. I will minimize *could've, should've, would've,* because I now know it wouldn't have made a difference.

Please continue to write this letter to yourself:

Worksheets

You have arrived at your destination, so are you ready to start your challenge? If you answered yes, *Good Luck.*

Reminder to self:
I understand toxic people – I do not personalize it
I will get to acceptance so I can continue to heal
I will own my hurt, pain, frustration, and disappointment and learn how I can be my best self
I will practice loving me

I have the choice to change when I am ready, and once I am ready to do this I will change. I can live a healthy and happier life because I believe in me, and I can do this!

Extremely important! Please don't give up. This does take time.

In this chapter you will find worksheets that will assist you in challenging your patterns and behaviors: core beliefs, expectations, irrational thoughts, attachments, toxicity.

- Month chart: Learn to raise awareness of actions, reactions, behaviors, patterns, accomplishments, reflections, on a daily basis

- A mood chart to track your mood and intensity:
    This is to be completed weekly
    This log will help you recognize your patterns

- Situational worksheet:
    Each log sheet is for you to use when a situation arises
    Date the top of the page
    Answer all the questions
    This will help you recognize your patterns
    Raise awareness of your feelings, emotions, toxicity, patterns, challenges

- Notes:
    Recognize all your hard work
    Write about how you feel
    Write what you have learned
    You can always go back for reinforcement of what you learned

Give yourself a pat on the back – You got this!

How to use the chart on the next page

Each day you are going to read over the listed questions and write in the numbers that apply to you in each box. You can copy this page so you can continue to go over the checklist for the next several weeks. Changing old actions, reactions, behaviors and recognizing patterns takes time.

Don't give up! You will get there!

Reminder:

1. **Educate** – you want to learn enough so you accept the diagnosis and don't personalize the personality
2. **Maintain boundaries**
3. **Effective communication**
4. **Don't get caught** in the chaos/drama
5. **Challenge** your irrational thoughts
6. **Stay grounded**

1. I enforced my boundaries
2. I did not personalize the other person's behaviors
3. I was clear in my communication
4. I used "I" statements
5. I recognized the toxicity
6. I did not participate in the chaos
7. I recognized the manipulation/gaslighting
8. I recognized the personality traits
9. I recognized my self doubt
10. I played the victim role
11. I felt guilt, pain, hurt
12. I believed the hurtful words said to me
13. I kept myself grounded
14. I educated myself on the toxicity
15. I felt I gained my power back
16. I continued to challenge my thoughts
17. I participated in a support group / attended therapy

Sun	Mon	Tue	Wed	Thurs	Fri	Sat

Mood Log

This worksheet will help you further recognize how you are feeling. Rate your mood at the end of each day.

Scale of 1 - 10

0--5--10

1 - 2: Calm, no impact; minimal reaction

3 - 4: Situation has you elevated, start to become defensive; tone gets louder, body language presents as guarded, angry, frustrated, anxious

5: Frustrated, annoyed; defensive mode

6 - 10: Anxiety is high, reaction is over the top; heated, angry, yelling, frustrated; defensive mode

Date	Anxiety Level	Irrational Thought

Challenge your toxic behaviors, irrational thoughts and core beliefs

On the next page are common key words to help you recognize patterns of behaviors, feelings and emotions you display during challenges and on a regular basis. These are related to your personality and can be influenced by the environment you've lived in and live in now.

The goal is to recognize these so you can change your life for the better.

Emotions, behaviors, feelings and characteristics

- ❑ Anxious
- ❑ Oversharing
- ❑ Feeling insecure
- ❑ Procrastinating
- ❑ Perfectionist
- ❑ Shame
- ❑ Emptiness
- ❑ Comparing myself to others
- ❑ Negative self talk
- ❑ People pleasing
- ❑ Personalizing
- ❑ Experience muscle tension
- ❑ Irritability
- ❑ Unable to sleep
- ❑ Difficulty concentrating
- ❑ Tired
- ❑ Headaches
- ❑ Restlessness
- ❑ Racing heart
- ❑ Indecisiveness
- ❑ Overthinking
- ❑ Trembling
- ❑ Nervousness
- ❑ Inability not to worry
- ❑ Sweating

- ❑ Intense fear of abandonment
- ❑ Walking on eggshells
- ❑ Impulsive
- ❑ Compromised my values
- ❑ Couldn't speak my mind
- ❑ Lying
- ❑ Jealousy
- ❑ Anger
- ❑ Deceived
- ❑ Paranoid
- ❑ Tolerating mean people
- ❑ Gaslighted
- ❑ Manipulated
- ❑ Hated
- ❑ Cheating
- ❑ Kept score
- ❑ Playing the victim
- ❑ Obsessed
- ❑ Justified heavior
- ❑ Dramatic
- ❑ Competetive
- ❑ Social isolation
- ❑ Overspending
- ❑ Use of profanity
- ❑ Aggression
- ❑ Stubborn/inflexible

Everything you have read has helped you gain understanding and clarity so you can start challenging toxic situations and people.

You have learned about toxicity, trauma, dependency, anxiety, negative core beliefs, expectations, and irrational thought patterns. You now have awareness, but don't assume and expect things to change overnight; it's a journey. Each day is a step forward, and even if you fall a few steps back – keep moving forward.

The next several pages are worksheets for challenging situations that arise; to help you process what happened with a logical mindset versus the emotional mind set.

Situation/Activating Event:

Reaction to situation: What fears and insecurities occurred? Did I experience anxiety and/or irrational thoughts? If I answered yes, what symptoms were present?

Did I overthink/ruminate/overexplain/justify the situation? How?

Did my expectations play a role in the situation? How?

Was I able to recognize the toxic tactics that occurred?

Did I recognize unhealthy attachment, trauma, and/or toxic behaviors?

Did I maintain my boundaries? Yes/No? Explain. How was my communication?

Did I lose myself in the toxicity?

Irrational thoughts, behaviors and patterns I will challenge:

Toxic behavior I will address:

Method I will use to ground myself and not personalize the situations of the toxic person:

Situation/Activating Event:

Reaction to situation: What fears and insecurities occurred? Did I experience anxiety and/or irrational thoughts? If I answered yes, what symptoms were present?

Did I overthink/ruminate/overexplain/justify the situation? How?

Did my expectations play a role in the situation? How?

Was I able to recognize the toxic tactics that occurred?

Did I recognize unhealthy attachment, trauma, and/or toxic behaviors?

Did I maintain my boundaries? Yes/No? Explain. How was my communication?

Did I lose myself in the toxicity?

Irrational thoughts, behaviors and patterns I will challenge:

Toxic behavior I will address:

Method I will use to ground myself and not personalize the situations of the toxic person:

Situation/Activating Event:

Reaction to situation: What fears and insecurities occurred? Did I experience anxiety and/or irrational thoughts? If I answered yes, what symptoms were present?

Did I overthink/ruminate/overexplain/justify the situation? How?

Did my expectations play a role in the situation? How?

Was I able to recognize the toxic tactics that occurred?

Did I recognize unhealthy attachment, trauma, and/or toxic behaviors?

Did I maintain my boundaries? Yes/No? Explain. How was my communication?

Did I lose myself in the toxicity?

Irrational thoughts, behaviors and patterns I will challenge:

Toxic behavior I will address:

Method I will use to ground myself and not personalize the situations of the toxic person:

Date _____ _____ _____

Situation/Activating Event:

Reaction to situation: What fears and insecurities occurred? Did I experience anxiety and/or irrational thoughts? If I answered yes, what symptoms were present?

Did I overthink/ruminate/overexplain/justify the situation? How?

Did my expectations play a role in the situation? How?

Was I able to recognize the toxic tactics that occurred?

Did I recognize unhealthy attachment, trauma, and/or toxic behaviors?

Did I maintain my boundaries? Yes/No? Explain. How was my communication?

Did I lose myself in the toxicity?

Irrational thoughts, behaviors and patterns I will challenge:

Toxic behavior I will address:

Method I will use to ground myself and not personalize the situations of the toxic person:

Situation/Activating Event:

Reaction to situation: What fears and insecurities occurred? Did I experience anxiety and/or irrational thoughts? If I answered yes, what symptoms were present?

Did I overthink/ruminate/overexplain/justify the situation? How?

Did my expectations play a role in the situation? How?

Was I able to recognize the toxic tactics that occurred?

Did I recognize unhealthy attachment, trauma, and/or toxic behaviors?

Did I maintain my boundaries? Yes/No? Explain. How was my communication?

Did I lose myself in the toxicity?

Irrational thoughts, behaviors and patterns I will challenge:

Toxic behavior I will address:

Method I will use to ground myself and not personalize the situations of the toxic person:

Situation/Activating Event:

Reaction to situation: What fears and insecurities occurred? Did I experience anxiety and/or irrational thoughts? If I answered yes, what symptoms were present?

Did I overthink/ruminate/overexplain/justify the situation? How?

Did my expectations play a role in the situation? How?

Was I able to recognize the toxic tactics that occurred?

Did I recognize unhealthy attachment, trauma, and/or toxic behaviors?

Did I maintain my boundaries? Yes/No? Explain. How was my communication?

Did I lose myself in the toxicity?

Irrational thoughts, behaviors and patterns I will challenge:

Toxic behavior I will address:

Method I will use to ground myself and not personalize the situations of the toxic person:

Reminders for me

Taking control of my life means I gave up fighting for something that isn't real. My silence means I'm tired of explaining myself. My silence means I am adapting to changes in my life. My silence means I'm on my self-healing journey that does not include you. My silence means I am moving on with love for myself.

I don't need to wonder where I stand with someone, because someone who truly appreciates me wouldn't have me questioning my sanity.

Sometimes closure is actions, not words. Close the book and don't expect a conversation.

It's time I let you go, as difficult as it is, but the pain is unhealthy for me. So, I'm cutting the cord that I should have cut a long time ago. This is me saying goodbye.

The day I leave you is the day I just say, "Fuck it; this is the day life gets a whole lot better."

I'm going to make sure in the next season of my life that I am not going to allow anyone to hurt me.

I am going to embrace the new life ahead of me.

A reminder that there's a difference between a person who hurts me by making a mistake, and a person who hurts me with their continued patterns. Patterns are not mistakes.

When I feel resentment, anger, and/or shame I will remind myself I am in a different place today. What was in the past stays in the pase. I did the best I was able to do and felt that was my only option for that *"tmoment and time in my life."*

My own personal reminders:

Self Exploration

What is the last compliment you received? How did it make you feel?

How can you improve your self-confidence?

What truths about yourself do you prefer to ignore?

What lies do you most often tell yourself?

I am making peace with my past. Forgiveness isn't letting people off the hook; it's emotional freedom for me.

Why or how are you a better person today than you were yesterday?

Write 3 things you are grateful for today:

"If you continue to think the way you've always thought, you'll continue to get what you've always got."
--Kevin Trudeau

Have you ever been lonely? How did you feel?

What is your biggest insecurity?

"When a negative thought enters your mind, think three positive ones. Train yourself to flip the script."
--Unknown

In what area are you lacking confidence?

What makes you feel optimistic?

"The way we see the problem is the problem."
--Stephen Covey

What bad habit(s) do you have? What are you going to do to change this habit? You can start now and change this habit for the next fourteen days.

Write down six positive affirmations that you can recite when you are overwhelmed, frustrated, angry, and/or disappointed.

"I've got 99 problems and 86 of them are completely made up scenarios in my head that I'm stressing about for absolutely no logical reason."
--Unknown

We all make mistakes in life, but that doesn't mean you have to pay for them for the rest of your life. It means you are human. What mistakes have you made?

What do you need to forgive yourself for?

"It's no use going back to yesterday, because I was a different person then."
--Lewis Carroll

How have you controlled the direction of your life this year?

What is keeping you from changing the things you'd like to change about yourself?

"Twenty years from now you'll be more disappointed by the things you did not do than the ones you did."
--Mark Twain

What lessons did you learn in the last year that changed your life?

What do you hope to move on from in the future?

"Mistakes are a fact of life. It is the response to the errors that counts."
--Nikki Giovanni

What experience(s) have taught you the most about life?

"Stop shrinking to fit into places you've outgrown."
--Unknown

Write the top 8 things in your life that cause you stress. For each stress factor, write what you can do to change it.

List four personal beliefs that you are willing to reconsider. Explain why.

"Never let yesterday use up too much of today."
--Will Rogers

What song describes your life? Why?

What movie describes your life? Why?

"Don't be afraid to change. You may lose something good, and you may gain something better."
--Unknown

How would you describe yourself to a stranger?

Does silence make you uncomfortable? Why?

"Never give up, because great things take time."
--Curiano

Check-in. Since starting this workbook, are you feeling more connected with yourself? How?

What is something you're grateful to have learned or done this week:

What I want to remember about today:

"You can waste your lives drawing lines. Or you can live your life crossing them."
--Shonda Rhimes

Are you truly living or just existing?

If you continue doing what you've been doing every day, where will you be in one year?

"Note to self: Small steps in the right direction are better than big steps in the wrong direction."
--Unknown

Check off the characteristics that you feel describe your personality. Write something about what you choose and add other characteristics you recognize about yourself.

- ❏ Practical
- ❏ Authentic
- ❏ Engaging
- ❏ Humble
- ❏ Good listener
- ❏ Reliable
- ❏ Patient
- ❏ Stubborn
- ❏ Trustworthy
- ❏ Forgiving
- ❏ Non-judgmental
- ❏ Resilient
- ❏ Calm
- ❏ Brave
- ❏ Fearless
- ❏ Inspiring
- ❏ Optimistic
- ❏ Supportive

"Look for something positive each day, even if some days you have to look a little harder."
--Unknown

Check off the characteristics that you feel describe your personality. Write something about what you choose and add other characteristics you recognize about yourself.

- ❑ Loyal

- ❑ Compassionate

- ❑ Generous

- ❑ Creative

- ❑ Passionate

- ❑ Kind

- ❑ Enthusiastic

- ❑ Self aware

- ❑ Intuitive

- ❑ Life learner

- ❑ Good listener

- ❑ A leader

- ❑ Unbiased

- ❑ Honest

- ❑ Wholehearted

- ❑ Committed

- ❑ Consistent

"The next best thing is the wrong thing, and the worst thing you can do is nothing."
--Theodore Roosevelt

"Reset.
Restart.
Refocus.
As many times as you need to."
--Steve Maraboli

I really wish others knew this about me:

What do you value the most about yourself?

"Stop being afraid of what could go wrong and think of what could go right."
--Unknown

Make a list of 5 of your negative personality traits.

Make a list of 5 of your positive personality traits.

"Start where you are. Use what you have. Do what you can."
--Arthur Ashe

When do you seek distractions? What are your distractions?

Which is worse: failing or never trying?

"There is only one thing that makes a dream impossible to achieve: the fear of failure."
--Paulo Coelho

Are you holding onto something you need to let go of?

What is your biggest regret?

"Turn your wounds into wisdom."
--Oprah Winfrey

Authentic or inauthentic self: It's a conscious choice of how we want to live and how we want to be seen. Think of yourself and define what authenticity means to you. Ask yourself, "Who am I supposed to be, and who am I?"

Sometimes we are bothered by outside noise – people telling us what to do, judging us and our opinions. How do you minimize the outside noise?

"I can't always control my thoughts, but I can choose how I respond to them."
--David Cuschieri

Being myself is hard because . . .

What matters most in your life?

"Don't be a victim of your negative thoughts."
--Unknown

"I am going to watch people's actions and recognize any attachment issues I may have and not be afraid to go for something better."

--Maria Shkreli

You live life every day as you know it, and one day life will come to an end. How would you respond to the following: You had all these opportunities to live your best life, pursue your dreams, find your true happiness, and notice you didn't follow through on many opportunities – what happened?

How would you answer this question?

"You can't always choose what happens to you, but you can always choose how you feel about it."
--Danielle Laporte

If you had the opportunity, what would you tell your childhood self?

"Train your mind to see the good in every situation."
--Unknown

What are you going to do today to be happier moving forward?

What is something you wish you did this year but didn't because you were afraid?

"A positive mind looks for ways it can done; A negative mind looks for ways it can't be done."
--Napoleon Hill

If you had more time to do what you love, what would you do?

How have you stepped out of your comfort zone this month?

"Worry doesn't empty tomorrow of its sorrows; it empties today of its strengths."
--Corrie ten Boom

I am going to make my life about . . .

How have you sabotaged yourself in the past three years?

"No one ever injured their eyesight by looking on the bright side."
--Unknown

Take time to reflect. How have you changed in the past 5 years? What have you learned?

Where do you see yourself in 5 years?

"Every day is a chance to be better."
--Unknown

One day I will look back at my life and my fears, hurt, and pain and remember I did the best I could at that time in my life. Sometimes it's the timing, sometimes it's the experience and sometimes it's just part of life. I'll remember to work differently and embrace **me** *moving forward.*

How old are you? How does it feel to be the age you are?

Do you like who you have become?

"Well done is better than well said."
--Benjamin Franklin

Where do you see yourself in 10 years?

"*Don't get upset with people or situations; both are powerless without your reaction.*"
--Unknown

What go-to coping strategies help you get through moments of emotional pain?

What battles have you fought and overcome in your life?

"Remember, you can't reach what's in front of you until you let go of what's behind you."
--Unknown

Do you seek external validation (parents, friends, social media) to feel complete?

Who do you compare yourself to? How does it make you feel?

"Your passion is waiting for your courage to catch up."
--Isabelle Lafleche

How do you handle anger and frustration?

What negative experiences seem to repeat in your life?

"The best way of learning about anything is by doing."
--Richard Branson

Make a list of everything you'd like to say yes to:

Make a list of everything you'd like to say no to:

"In any given moment we have two options: to step forward into growth or to step back into safety."
--Abraham Maslow

Do you consider yourself non-judgmental? Are you open-minded? Do you seek to understand others before jumping to conclusions?

What do you take for granted?

"Do not learn how to react. Learn how to respond!"
--Buddha

When setting goals, are you **Interested** (you come up with excuses for why you can't do these goals) or are you **Committed** (you do whatever it takes to meet these goals)? Which are you?

"All you can change is yourself, but sometimes that changes everything!"
--Gary W. Goldstein

Love yourself the best you can.

Every month for the next six months, you are going to do something different. You are going to do something new: get out of your rut, say yes to something you would normally say no to, start a hobby, get a different haircut, wear different clothing, try a new activity. It can be anything, and you are going to do it. Write about all these new experiences here.

"Happiness is not by chance, but by choice."
--Jim Rohn

Write a letter to someone who believed in you when you didn't believe in yourself.

"If opportunity doesn't knock, build a door."
--Kurt Cobain

Go back to a time when you were hurt. Write a letter to the person who hurt you, explaining to them how they hurt you. At the end, forgive them.

"We aren't given a good life or a bad life. We are given a life. It's up to us to make it good or bad."
--Unknown

Write a letter to your future self, describing your life story.

Write a thank-you letter to yourself.

"Life is a one-time offer. Live it well."
--Unknown

Write a letter to your future self, asking for guidance and everything else you need on the way to becoming the best version of yourself.

"Don't be afraid to start over. This time you're not starting from scratch, you're starting from Experience." --Unknown

Gratitude. Reflect on the good and bad things that happen to you and what you did to make the bad things more positive.

"The future belongs to those who believe in the beauty of their dreams."
--Eleanor Roosevelt

Clearing out your head space

Okay, time for brutal honesty with yourself. Write down your anger, pain, hate, bad thoughts, and wishes. Once you've written it all down, read over what you've written, tear out that page, and burn it.

Take control and close these deep wounds so you can move forward. No person deserves to have this much control over you.

"Yesterday I was clever, so I wanted to change the world. Today I am wise, so I am changing myself."
--Rumi

Letting go

Eventually the coupons of fault and blame of others expire and keeping the past in your present no longer serves you. It's time to let go and enjoy the journey ahead, making the best of each day and having peace with yourself. The moment you start to be in control of your life, the empowerment will feel like something you never could have imagined. Sometimes this happens when we push ourselves through our trauma and sometimes it happens when at any moment, we have an epiphany and say, "I'm done with the hurt and I'm done with letting people hurt me." Whatever way your healing comes, that's how its meant to, and always remind yourself: **it's your choice.**

I can choose to sit in my pain and not work on me, or I can choose to not let my past hurt me and embrace my life ahead of me because I can control it.
I have broken up with TOXICITY.

Congratulations and keep moving forward. When you get to this place, you have options to close the past.

1. Reflect on this workbook and recognize how far you've come.
2. When you're ready, tear out pages 6-20 and have a bonfire. Tear them up; burn them.
3. When you're ready, tear out pages 21-28 and have a bonfire. Tear them up; burn them.
4. When you're ready, tear out pages 29-48 and have a bonfire. Tear them up; burn them.
5. When you're ready, tear out pages 49-54 and have a bonfire. Tear them up; burn them.
6. When you're ready, tear out pages 55-64 and have a bonfire. Tear them up; burn them.
7. When you're ready, tear out pages 65-70 and have a bonfire. Tear them up; burn them
8. When you're ready, tear out pages 71-96 and have a bonfire. Tear them up; burn them
9. When you're ready, tear out pages 97-108 and have a bonfire. Tear them up; burn them

1. Write a note to yourself about how far you've come and how you've found closure from toxicity.
2. When you're ready to close the past, have a bonfire, tear up and burn the rest of the book.

"Sometimes when you're in a dark place you think you've been buried but you've actually been planted."
--Christine Caine

*"**Keep looking up**...that's the secret of life."*

--*Charlie Brown*

Made in the USA
Middletown, DE
21 January 2023

22222838R00104